The DEFENSE
DIARIES *of*
W. Morgan Petty

The DEFENSE DIARIES *of* *W. Morgan Petty*

EDITED BY BRIAN BETHELL

PANTHEON BOOKS, NEW YORK

Library of Congress Cataloging in Publication Data

Bethell, Brian.
The defense diaries of W. Morgan Petty.

I. Title.
PR6052.E83D4   1985   823'.914   84-22767
ISBN 0-394-73263-4

Manufactured in the United States of America

First American Edition

They may not frighten the enemy
But by God they frighten me . . .

The Duke of Wellington

For Holly Bethell
In the hope that you may read this
to your grandchildren

Foreword

The first time I had the pleasure of meeting W. Morgan Petty was at the Garden Centre. I had gone to pick up some fish food and he, along with Roger, was loading bamboo canes into the back of a Morris Minor. Learning of my interest in alternative defence he was happy, after the usual security check, to show me his own modest experiment in that direction, the Nuclear Free Zone at 3 Cherry Drive. I must admit that early on I was very sceptical of the viability of such a zone. However, armed with a sheaf of government booklets and newspaper cuttings, and displaying infinite patience, he explained his plan in detail. Furthermore, as he pointed out, if no less a person than George Bush, the Vice President of the United States, thought nuclear war survivable, who was he to argue? Not for Morgan Petty the hole in the ground covered by earth, the tinned food and the chemical toilet. Far safer, he reasoned, to be out of the mess altogether with a nuclear free declaration and then, whatever happened, his afternoon routine of a little light weeding followed by tea on the patio would remain undisturbed.

That evening as I was about to depart I cited John Donne's thoughts that 'No man is an island'. Morgan Petty smiled politely and suggested that Mr Donne had made a mistake.

Sunday, 13 February 1983

A cold bright day. Roger, who comes in to help with the garden, has picked two pounds of firm round sprouts. They do taste so much better with a frost on them. Over coffee, he tells me of a very interesting interview he has heard with an American general. According to Roger, this general had every confidence that a nuclear war could be confined to a small area. I must say I find this very comforting, as neither Roger nor myself has any argument with the Super Powers, and it therefore seems only logical that, should they need to have a nuclear war, they should pick a small area well away from us.

Tuesday, 15 February

Roger has put up a sign at the end of the garden. It reads: 'NUCLEAR WAR – KEEP OUT'. It is intended, so he tells me, to denote the point at which our garden begins and protagonists in a nuclear war should cease hostilities. I must say that I have reservations about the position of the sign vis-à-vis the privet hedge. I think it makes the hedge's position ambiguous. Furthermore, it is not a very big sign and I have doubts whether it could be seen by a reconnaissance aircraft. I was going to mention these points to Roger, but he broke the handle on his hedge clippers earlier and was in a bit of a mood so I stayed silent. I did, however, point out that the text 'NUCLEAR WAR – KEEP OUT' could have an unsettling effect on the neighbours, who might think we were planning to have one in the garden. On reflection I realize this was a mistake, as Roger pulled up the sign, put down his spade and went off in a huff.

Tuesday, 22 February

We have now tried various ways of denoting our perimeters but to no avail. Even what I thought was Roger's brilliant idea of painting the trees with luminous paint so that combatants

NUCLEAR FREE ZONE, 3 CHERRY DRIVE

Cherry Drive

No. 3

would still be aware of our borders at night was not a great success. Furthermore, he backed into a tree in the dark and now has paint on his new anorak. After much thought, Roger and I agree that it would probably be much easier to formally declare 3 Cherry Drive a Nuclear Free Zone. Unfortunately I cannot write to Mrs Thatcher and Mr Andropov this evening as Roger has used the last of the envelopes for storing his brassica seed.

Wednesday, 23 February

The big day. I have posted off a letter to Mr Andropov, the Soviet leader, explaining my decision to declare my house and garden a Nuclear Free Zone and enclosing a diagram. This zone runs from the shiplap fencing in the east, along the fence, up past the greenhouse and fishpond to the pavement in the west. The pavement isn't actually mine but I have included it in the zone because, although it belongs to the council, it would be a bit difficult to get around the back of the house if it were destroyed in a thermonuclear exchange. I have requested that Mr Andropov pass this diagram on to whoever is responsible for destroying this part of Kent, asking them to be very careful to avoid us. I have further suggested that he might like to formalize our state of non-aggression by means of a treaty, and that we talk it over one weekend when he's not busy. I have also contacted Mrs Thatcher, making her aware of our situation. Both Roger and myself have often heard her say how much she is in favour of breaking down the big state monopolies and introducing an element of competition. What better way for her to do this to the biggest state monopoly of all – defence – than by lending her support to people like us?

Thursday, 24 February

After the heady wine of our declaration, I am now faced with a number of practical problems, not least of which is the fact that I have never conducted bilateral arms negotiations before, and am not entirely sure how I should go about them. The nearest I have come to such a situation was the refereeing of a chess tournament. Unfortunately, on that occasion the clocks that timed the participants' decisions went wrong, leading to some very acrimonious exchanges. Roger, who seems in a much better humour since he got the motor mower to work, mentioned that Mr Reagan had just sacked Eugene Rostow. I had to admit that I didn't know who Eugene Rostow was. According to Roger he was, until his dismissal, the leader of an arms reduction team in Geneva, and Roger suggested that as Mr Rostow is out of work, and doubtless short of cash, he might give us a crash course, by post, in the conducting of arms negotiations. I wonder how much he charges per hour for such tuition? I can only hope they don't have time clocks at arms talks.

Monday, 28 February

Five whole days since our declaration and no invasion. Some time ago I saw Mr Heseltine, the Secretary of State for Defence, on television. He made the point that, but for the nuclear deterrent, the Soviet Union would overrun the West. I must say that this has not been our experience. Perhaps tomorrow I will wake up and find the garden full of Russian soldiers but, up to now, everything has been very quiet. We did have a visit from a shifty-looking character who claimed that he was selling double glazing; it could be that he was a K.G.B. agent spying out the land for an attack. I will be happier when we have concluded our non-aggression treaty. Tonight I shall drop Mr Heseltine a line; no doubt, given his television statements, he will be very interested to monitor the situation here. Roger has meanwhile been sorting through our weapons of conventional defence and informs me that they consist of one nearly new garden fork and a bayonet his grandfather brought back from the 1914–18 war which has recently been used for splitting logs. Not much to hold the Red

Army back with I will admit. I have asked Roger to dig a shelter when the weather improves, and whilst I know Mr Heseltine is a busy man, given his strong commitment to defence, I shall ask him if he can spare a couple of days to help.

Tuesday, 1 March

Roger comes in to tell me that he will need some money to put a new handle on the second of our garden forks. This he says will increase our defence capability by some fifty per cent. On opening up our Defence Fund, I discover that it contains only twenty-eight pounds. Once the handle has been paid for we shall have less than eighteen and we still have to pay Mr Rostow for his lessons in arms control. Fortunately, it looks as though we have been saved by coincidence. Letitia, one of the Odette sisters, dropped in for a seed box Roger had promised her. Over a cup of tea, I explained that we had declared the house and garden a Nuclear Free Zone. I said that it was proving expensive and would doubtless continue to do so. Letitia says they were discussing arms expenditure at her knitting circle only last week and that Mrs Porter, who does the fastest plain and purl she's ever seen, told her that it costs the United States government six hundred pounds per year to protect every man, woman and child in Western Europe. If this is the case, then by taking over our own international security we are saving the American government some twelve hundred pounds a year. I shall drop a line to the Secretary of the United States Treasury and ask if they would be prepared to donate half of this saving to help us over our cash-flow problem. Roger says that if I mention mending the garden fork I should refer to it as 'an implement used in horticultural activity situations which also forms an integral part of our conventional defence equipment', as this is the sort of language they understand. I just hope they don't send us the cash in dollars as I am not sure they accept these at the hardware shop.

Thursday, 3 March

This morning I received a postcard from the Ministry of Defence informing me that the principal private secretary to the Secretary of State acknowledges receipt of my letter which is receiving attention. Things are moving at last. Just as Roger and I settled down for elevenses, an aircraft roared overhead. My first thought was that Mr Heseltine's doubts had been confirmed, and Roger and I, armed with bayonet and garden fork, raced out to face the attack. However, it appears that it was a false alarm, caused, says Mr Bridger (who prunes the trees locally and was tending a bonfire), by a low-flying jet with U.S.A.F. markings. Even though this was a false alarm, it still presents us with a problem. If United States aircraft continue to fly over our Nuclear Free Zone then we could still provide a target for retaliation. I shall drop a line to the United States Strategic Air Command in Omaha and acquaint them with the position. I shall leave Roger to draft the letter as he is so much better at the American language.

Friday, 4 March

Rain. Roger, who had hoped to fork over some of the vegetable patch and lay out the area for the anti-tank ditch behind the rhododendrons, spent the morning instead on the draft letter to the United States Strategic Air Command. At lunchtime he showed it to me and I must admit to being very impressed. He has asked that they exclude this area from any nuclear strike scenario they may have prepared. He goes on to explain that our wood, brick and vegetative location (house and garden), outlined on the enclosed plan, and the elevatory nimbus and cumulus area (sky) above the wood, brick and vegetative location is a Nuclear Free Zone, and ends with the warning that military use of this nimbus and cumulus area might jeopardize the continued viability situation (existence) of the wood, brick and vegetative location. I knew I was right to ask him to do it. I did, however, express the view that the diagram might not give the U.S.A.F. enough detail to enable them to distinguish our garden from the others. However, according to Roger, military satellites are capable of reading the print on newspapers from three miles up. If that is the case, then they should have no difficulty in recognizing my garden. It has the only pond in Cherry Drive with two Koi carp in it, something I shall point out in the finished letter. I shall also ask, without Roger's knowledge, that when they are going to take the pictures they give us a few days' notice as I know Roger would like to be in them and how he always likes to dress up for the camera.

I am disappointed that we have not yet heard from Mr Andropov but doubtless he will want to discuss our proposals with Mr Gromyko, who, according to Roger, is still in Western Germany. I am a little concerned about protocol for Mr Andropov's visit here. I resolve to contact Her Majesty the Queen; the last thing I want to do is cause a diplomatic incident. As Mr Andropov is a head of state the Queen may want to come herself, or delegate one of the minor royals. It is a decision I shall leave to the Palace. If Her Majesty wishes to meet him in the living room here, where I intend to hold the talks, I am just wondering whether we have enough chairs and good china. As to refreshments, I shall ask Letitia's sister, Viola, if she will make me some of her special shortbread, and, given the numbers we expect, I will also try and borrow a tea urn.

Saturday, 5 March

Today we hold our first parade, Roger in his overalls with garden fork at the ready. I must confess my eyes moisten with pride at the sight of him standing there prepared to face the enemy hordes. It was a pity that when I called him to attention he slammed the fork down with such force that the handle broke off. What we really need is better equipment, but we have still not received our six hundred pounds from the United States and, after buying two sun hats, which we have dyed khaki, there is only nine pounds and some change left in the Defence Fund. We need to get hold of some cut-price weaponry. Roger suggests N A T O might have some. Of course, now he has got the garden ready for spring planting and the hedge and bushes are in bud, we will have to look for something that can be used with the minimum of horticultural damage. What we really want is something capable of 'taking out' a T54 tank, but leaving the privet hedge next to it unharmed. Roger has also expressed an interest in acquiring a 'noddy suit'. Apparently these have been developed as protection from chemical warfare, but he is convinced they would be just right for spraying the roses.

Monday, 7 March

Roger has taken to reading the *Guardian* newspaper. I think he has been influenced by all those people on television who buy it. He tells me some of them are almost famous, but I have to admit I don't recognize anyone. He shows me a cutting he has taken, which expresses doubts about the National Health Service's ability to cope with the casualties resulting from a nuclear strike. I assure him that we are quite safe behind our borders and he goes off, I think happily, to put the cauliflower seed in the propagator. However, he has planted some doubts in my mind. Roger was in the Scouts, where he earned his First Aid badge, and so he should be quite capable of dealing with cuts and bruises, but what would happen in an emergency? We both still have our appendix, not to mention the fact that I suffer from chronic catarrh, a condition that would undoubtedly be worsened by post-nuclear conditions. Where for example would I get a prescription and, more important, where would it be dispensed? I have seen Mr Clarke, the Health Minister, on television several times lately. I'm afraid he reminds me of a doctor we had once at school who used to smile and tell you it wouldn't hurt a bit just before he caused you great pain with a needle. In the chaos that would follow a thermonuclear exchange I wonder if there is any benefit in going private?

Wednesday, 9 March

No bed until 4.00 a.m. for the defenders of 3 Cherry Drive. A night-time exercise in which Roger and myself test our 'flexible response' strategy, maintaining a front-line post down by the compost heap until overrun and then falling back to a secondary position behind the hyacinths. Unfortunately, between these two battle lines lies the pond, and in his eagerness to retreat Roger lost his footing and splashed in, causing the cancellation of the exercise. The Koi carp look no worse for the experience but Roger was soaked through and spent two hours sitting in the kitchen wrapped in a blanket and drinking Lemsip. I have a nasty suspicion he may be developing a cold, and this at the busiest time of the year in the garden. I was just thinking nothing else could go wrong when Mr Oliver, a friend of Roger's from the Camera Club, delivered the *Guardian*. Now it appears that the new American Pershing I I missiles have problems with their guidance systems and are not landing quite where they should. This is just the sort of day when, if the United States fired off a missile, intending to demolish Vladivostok, it would land in the middle of our garden, and this after all the hard work Roger has put in on the seed beds. I shall have to seek urgent clarification on this.

Thursday, 10 March

I am sometimes driven to wonder who poses the biggest danger to us here, the Super Powers or ill-considered remarks by ministers in Whitehall? Someone I've never heard of called Peter Blaker, who is, it seems, quite junior at the Ministry of Defence, described those in favour of unilateral disarmament as 'woolly minds in woolly hats'. I suppose he thought he was being clever. However, his remarks have caused problems here in Cherry Drive. He could not have known, I suppose, that Roger wears a red and white balaclava in cold weather. The result is that, already showing signs of flu, he has taken the remark very much to heart and has gone off in a sulk. Time that he should have spent digging the anti-tank ditch behind the rhododendron bushes has been spent inside the shed doing the *Guardian* crossword. He was extremely sharp when I pointed out that he'd got nine across wrong. I am sure that Mr Blaker didn't intend the remark for Roger personally, and so I have dropped him a line asking for a brief note making that point which I hope will placate Roger and get him back both on defence work and clearing the early nettles from around the greenhouse. I have come to the conclusion that what we need is some sound military advice and, as a consequence, have approached Field Marshal Lord Carver for his assessment of our military position, especially as I suspect the ground between the raspberries and strawberries to be wide open to an attack by fast-moving armour. Perhaps he will be able to spend a few days down here in the dining room going over my plans. At the very least he may, like Roger's grandfather, have some souvenirs from his army days that would help in our defence, and might consider donating them. Maybe he has another bayonet. But what I'm really looking for is a sixty-millimetre howitzer.

Monday, 14 March

A letter arrives from Field Marshal Lord Carver. Now that's what I call military efficiency. Unfortunately he tells me that he cannot spare the time for a personal reconnaissance of our position, but he provides very useful logistical information about warning devices, the positioning of anti-tank weapons, etc. He also recommends preparation for a gas attack (we still have not heard from NATO headquarters about Roger's 'noddy suit') and suggests a rota for sentry duty. It is easy to see how he became a Field Marshal. On the equipment front he has offered me a Swedish cavalry officer's sword, and all this despite the fact that my letter, like all our defence correspondence, was sent recorded delivery which resulted in the postman waking him up.

House of Lords

12 March 1963

Dear Mr. Petty,

I am afraid that I cannot spare the time to do a personal reconnaissance of your defensive positions. My advice would be to sow anti-tank and anti-personnel mines liberally in your flower-beds, as well as surrounding your property with warning sensors of every description. An effective anti-tank guided weapon in every upstairs bedroom window would seem to be essential. You and Roger will need infra-red binoculars to see the target at night. Don't forget the danger of chemical warfare. You should better wear anti-gas equipment at all times, including at night. You may get a little short of sleep, so you should work out a roster to take turns to act as sentry.

I am afraid that the only weapon I can spare from the defence of this area is a Swedish cavalry officer's sword. If you can leave Roger in charge while you gallop over here on your charger, I would gladly hand it over to you.

It appears that you are an ideal recruit for the new Home Defence Force which my erstwhile colleague, Admiral of the Fleet Lord Kill-Nation is sponsoring. I am sure he would welcome you into the ranks, even though you may be taking rather too broad a view of the Home Defence for his liking.

Yours sincerely,

Michael Curver tm

Editor's note: Here follows a transcript of Lord Carver's letter.

B.B.

12 March 1983

Dear Mr Petty,

I am afraid that I cannot spare the time to do a personal reconnaissance of your defensive positions. My advice would be to sow anti-tank and anti-personnel mines liberally in your flower-beds, as well as surrounding your property with warning sensors of every description. An effective anti-tank guided weapon in every upstairs bedroom window would seem to be essential. You and Roger will need infra-red binoculars to see the target at night. Don't forget the danger of chemical warfare. You should both wear anti-gas equipment at all times, including at night. You may get a bit short of sleep, so you should work out a roster to take turns to act as sentry.

I am afraid that the only weapon I can spare from the defence of this area is a Swedish cavalry officer's sword. If you can leave Roger in charge while you gallop over here on your charger, I would gladly hand it over to you.

It appears that you are an ideal recruit for the new Home Defence Force which my erstwhile colleague, Admiral of the Fleet Lord Hill-Norton, is sponsoring. I am sure he would welcome you into the ranks, even though you may be taking rather too local a view of Home Defence for his liking.

> Yours sincerely,
> Michael Carver FM

P.S. Don't send me any more letters by Recorded Delivery. The postman comes before I am up, and I have to go to Fareham to collect them. M.C.

Tuesday, 15 March

Another bright but cold day. Roger and Mr Bridger spent the morning clearing around the bulbs. It's so nice to see spring arrive and everything in bud. What a shame Mr Bridger, while carrying weeds to the incinerator, fell over the wire Roger had strung between the Jubilee roses as part of last week's anti-guerrilla-warfare exercise. I am sure I told Roger to take this down during weeding. According to a very indignant Mr Bridger, Roger just stood there and laughed, and now an atmosphere has developed between them. Currently, Roger is planning this year's floral arrangements in the garden, with the added advantage that he has the earth from the anti-tank ditch to build steps in the flower beds. He has asked that I write to the British Museum as he thinks that, given our nuclear free status, they might loan us one or two of their statues. He'd like to use these as the centrepiece in 'A Tribute to the Roman Empire', the theme he has chosen for this year, placing them under the magnolia tree and surrounding them with sweet williams. Thus, not only would we have an excellent arrangement but, should there be a nuclear holocaust whilst they are in our possession, they will be saved for posterity.

What a very good idea.

Thursday, 17 March

Loud voices drew me to the window after lunch to see Roger and Mr Bridger in heated discussion. It seems an argument has developed over whether or not 'fall-out' is worse than greenfly. Roger took the position that nothing could be as bad as the greenfly he had to contend with in 1974, after a damp spring. But Mr Bridger was adamant that 'fall-out' was worse for discolouring soft fruit and impairing its jam-making qualities. Further disagreement exists over its effect on courgettes and tomatoes, with Mr Bridger asserting that it will affect their moisture content. As both consider themselves expert gardeners, I fear this argument might run and run, especially after Tuesday's incident. I have therefore offered to approach the Secretary of State at the Department of Agriculture to get a ruling from him and a recommendation, if possible, for a non-chemical spray to deal with this 'fall-out'.

Saturday, 19 March

I have received a reply to my letter to the Prime Minister from somebody called S.M. Williams. It is very short and to the point, and enclosed with it is a list of arms control negotiations in which Britain is involved. I must say that with all these negotiations taking place I am surprised no progress has yet been made. I showed this list to Roger, who complained that it does not include our own overtures to Mr Andropov. I pointed out that it was prepared before the government was aware of our involvement, and that doubtless our modest efforts would be included in the reprint. I am, however, a little puzzled because, whilst it is signed by a member of the Defence Department, the notepaper is that of the Foreign and Commonwealth Office. I can only assume from this that, given our new status, we are to be treated, for official purposes, as a foreign state. I just hope this won't cause any problems with postage or on the buses.

Tuesday, 22 March

Mr Bridger called in with several bags of well rotted horse manure. It seems he promised it to Roger for the vegetables. I suspect this manure is by way of a peace offering after their recent disagreements. When he arrived, Roger was out at the doctor's, having a boil lanced, and I welcomed the opportunity to have a quiet word. Mr Bridger, as well as being an authority on leaf mould and big bud, is a man of great military experience, having spent seven years in the Army Catering Corps, reaching the rank of corporal. I explained to him that I had seen pictures on the television news of the new Challenger tank. There it was, speeding across open ground, flattening everything in its path. It occurred to me then that this was just what we needed here. Mr Bridger agreed, telling me how, during his time in the army, the tank was the thing the soldiers feared most after his plum duff. I think he was joking but didn't dare laugh because I was not sure. I have,

Foreign and Commonwealth Office
London SW1A 2AH

Telephone 01-

W Morgan Petty
3 Cherry Drive
Canterbury
Kent

Your reference

Our reference

Date
        17 March 1983

Dear Mr Morgan-Petty,

Thank you for your letter of 23 February to the Prime Minister and
for keeping her informed of your correspondence with Mr Andropov. I
am enclosing a leaflet which we have just issued which describes the
various arms control negotiations in which Britain is involved.

Yours sincerely,
Stephen Williams

S M Williams
Defence Department

therefore, resolved that we shall have a Challenger for Cherry Drive, and to that end I have written to the Royal Ordnance Factory in Leeds, where I understand they are manufactured, with some preliminary questions.

Wednesday, 23 March

Roger has been extremely sullen today. At first I thought it was just one of his moods, or the after-effects of having his boil lanced. Eventually, however, I found out that it's due to his concern about the effect the increasing Super-Power tension is having on his nest egg. It is not a great deal of money, a bit put by each week, plus a little his grandmother left him. He was intending to remove it from his post office account during periods of high international tension and keep it with him. However, this would involve the risk of loss or theft, and furthermore, as these periods of high international tension are on the increase, he would be spending most of his time in front of the post office counter. On the other hand, should a thermo-nuclear exchange take place before he can withdraw the money, then at best he will have to go to another post office should his own be destroyed, entailing a mountain of form-filling, or at worst never see his money again. I must admit this has made me very concerned about my own modest invest-ments in savings certificates. Where, if the post office has been demolished, am I to encash these when they mature? Un-doubtedly the government has made provisions for just such an emergency, and I shall ask the Treasury this evening for a breakdown of their post-nuclear savings redemption plan.

Friday, 25 March

8.00 a.m. And so ends another night exercise. We had intended to try out our new pincer movement, trapping a frontal assault from behind the greenhouse, between the hyacinths and the laurel bush. I am fairly confident that once checked at the laurel bush we could regroup and push the enemy back. Roger has developed an explosive device using baked bean tins and weedkiller (a trick taught him by Mr Bridger), and the original idea was to test this device on the lily pond as a deterrent to amphibious attacks. However, the goldfish and frogs have spawned early and, in the interests of conservation, these tests will have to wait. This did not prevent Roger from trying out, against my advice, his baked-bean-tin bomb. Unfortunately there was not a long enough fuse, and no sooner had he touched it with a match than it exploded. I am pleased to say that, although shaken, he seems all right, if a little covered in soot. Whilst there is nothing lacking in our enthusiasm, I feel that the gaps in our military knowledge are obvious. I wonder whether they have a course for people like us at the Royal Military Academy, Sandhurst? It would need to be a sandwich course because of Roger's commitments in the garden. Maybe they could supply a prospectus and scale of fees?

Sunday, 27 March

Today when I take Roger his mid-morning cup of coffee I find him not, as I expected, sowing the first of the early peas, but asleep under some sacking in the shed. I was tempted to wake him, but reflected on the fact that he had not finished sentry duty until three this morning. It should also not be forgotten that he spent the twenty-four hours before that stringing twine and baked bean tins around our perimeter – what he, now that he uses the American language in defence matters, calls 'an enemy warning announcement system'. I must confess that I am feeling the strain myself, what with the endless hours over the map table trying to find a defensive posture that would stop a frontal assault securing the greenhouse. I think that before we both collapse with exhaustion we should look for some help. I know Mr Bridger offered to take a turn as sentry, but his eyesight is not what it was, and, fired with all his old military determination, he might run Roger or myself through with the garden fork. Roger tells me that Norman Tebbit, the

Secretary of State for Employment, has been busy building up the jobless, although I am not sure why. I must confess I can't tell one of Mrs Thatcher's ministers from another – they all look so alike. According to Roger, Mr Tebbit is the tall, bald one with the look of a mortician. With so many people on his books it seems logical that Mr Tebbit should have a suitable recruit to help us here at Cherry Drive. Of course any such help would have to be of the very highest quality as, in the event of an attack, we would expect to be outnumbered several thousands to one. What we really need is an urban guerrilla with an interest in gardening, so that he can give Roger a hand in between exercises. On the question of remuneration, Roger suggests that something called the Manpower Services Commission will pay anyone to do anything as long as they are off the list of unemployed. That settles that problem at least.

Tuesday, 29 March

More bad news about the United States Pershing I I missiles. It seems that they are still not landing in the proper place, frequently demolishing barns on farms near to their testing range in the Mid West. Although he has not said anything since we received this news, it is clearly worrying Roger. With the first of the vegetables in, he faces the prospect, should we be visited by a rogue missile, of having to do all that work again. Letitia Odette called round and asked to borrow a trowel. I could see that Roger was not too keen; he can be very proprietorial about his tools. However, her visit may turn out to have been a blessing in disguise. Being eighty, the Odette sisters are only a little younger than President Reagan, and they watch all his speeches. Letitia tells me that recently he was talking of a new United States defence system which uses microwaves to deflect missiles heading for a target. If it can deflect missiles aimed at a target, it stands to reason it could also deflect missiles heading towards an area by mistake. If this system does work on the principle of microwaves, then Roger wonders whether we could convert our oven, which also works on microwaves, to double as a deflective device. It might be that we would have to get another microwave oven to deal with rogue missiles separately. More expense. I shall have to make inquiries.

Thursday, 7 April

A depressing morning going over the accounts. Three pounds thirty pence in the Defence Fund. Still, I'm sure something will turn up. I have dropped a line to Geoffrey Pattie, who is in charge of something called 'weapons procurement' (which I think is a fancy name for buying guns) at the Ministry of Defence, asking him to keep his eyes open, as he jets around the world, for a cheap job lot of weapons. I am sure that tucked away under a tarpaulin in some remote corner of the globe, there is just what we're looking for. Though heaven knows how we are going to pay for them. Perhaps, given that we usually woefully over-produce in the vegetable garden, we could barter some sacks of potatoes or string beans for rifles and artillery pieces. I'm sure these would be much better for the countries involved.

Friday, 8 April

Roger has come up with a brilliant idea. He suggests we hold a 'Challenger for Cherry Drive' Bring and Buy Sale cum Tombola to raise money for our tank. It is such a simple solution to our problem I wonder why I never thought of it. Still, Roger is the one with seven O-levels. I was hoping that Viola Odette, who plays the piano, would provide the music, but according to Roger she is having trouble with her legs again, and so I shall approach the London Symphony Orchestra to see if they can take her place. On the question of refreshments, I heard recently that a Lady Olga Maitland had set up a group called 'Women for Defence'. I wonder if they would be willing to roll up their sleeves and bake the necessary jam tarts, Victoria sponges, chocolate gateaux, etc., for the cake stall which is always such a central part of these things? I shall ask them.

Monday, 11 April

Mr Oliver, from the Camera Club, came around with his Yashica. It appears that he is having shutter trouble again, and wanted Roger's help. When I went into the kitchen there were bits of camera all over the table and both men were on their hands and knees looking for a lost part. Mr Oliver does not approve of our Nuclear Free Zone and resents the time Roger spends on it. Time which, he said today, Roger should spend behind the enlarger. I countered by saying that if it wasn't for our nuclear free status there would be nobody around to look at Roger's pictures after a thermonuclear exchange. A point to me, I think. When he had gone, still without finding the missing part, Roger said he was concerned about the legality of our keeping pieces of artillery, when we get them, here at Cherry Drive. A thought put into his head, no doubt, by Mr Oliver. His grandfather it seems had a scatter gun he used for scaring pigeons away from his brassicas, which he was only allowed to keep on the condition that it was locked up in a cupboard under the stairs. Roger is a meticulous observer of the law (I remember how distressed he was when he was fined for double parking outside the tree nursery) and I could see that my explanation that we didn't need a licence as these were for purely defensive purposes had not entirely satisfied him. Obviously if we were allowed to keep our artillery on the same basis as the conditions attached to Roger's grandfather's scatter gun, this would present us with enormous problems, not the least of which would be how to get a sixty-millimetre howitzer under the stairs. Making my cocoa this evening, I stepped back and heard a crunching noise. I have found the missing part. Hurriedly, I put it in the waste bin. No point in making unnecessary waves.

Wednesday, 13 April

In the post this morning is a letter from the headquarters of the Royal Ordnance Factory. It seems that the cost of a new Challenger tank is greater than I had anticipated – depressing, because there is less than a pound in the Defence Fund. Neither do they do easy terms. Instead, they suggest that I negotiate a loan with my bank manager – difficult, in that I do not have one. Still, it does seem that we can have the colour we want. Roger thinks blue would be nice, but I favour maroon. All we have to do now is raise one and a half million pounds.

Thursday, 14 April

A note to the Prime Minister. I am afraid I have to tell her that we have not, as yet, heard from Mr Andropov. I am sure that he intends to reply and am comforted when Roger tells me he read in the *Daily Mail* that the postal system in the Soviet Union is as bad as in the WI district of London. I am sure that she will be pleased to hear that we have not suffered an invasion since we acquired nuclear free status, and even more pleased to learn of our intention to buy British, in the form of a Challenger tank, rather than go abroad for our military hardware. I have taken the liberty of asking her for a little something for our White Elephant Stall. There has been, of late, a great deal of talk about Mrs Thatcher calling a general election soon, and I have also asked if, when she decides on the date, she could give us a few days' notice prior to the announcement. In which case I could send Roger off to the local bookmaker to place a wager. I am not normally a betting man – the occasional sweepstake ticket for charity – but this is, after all, a very good cause.

Friday, 15 April

Roger presents me with a plan for strengthening our air

From: Peter McLoughlin   Director Sales & Marketing

PROCUREMENT EXECUTIVE
MINISTRY OF DEFENCE

HEADQUARTERS ROYAL ORDNANCE FACTORIES

St. Christopher House, Southwark Street
LONDON, SE1 0TD

Telephone: 01-928 7999, ext

W Morgan Petty Esq
3 Cherry Drive
Canterbury
Kent   11 April 1983

Dear Mr Petty,

        Your letter to ROF Leeds has been sent to me for reply
because I am responsible within the ROFs for the sale of
Challenger.

        I was delighted that you found our unveiling ceremony
impressive and flattered that your self defence organisation
is interested in the acquisition of this superlative fighting
vehicle.

        The answer to your specific questions are as follows:

        i.   We only normally sell the vehicles to fleet customers
        when the cost of the vehicle, spares, training etc would
        be something of the order of £1.5 million.

        ii. We are not, unfortunately, able to offer any easy
        terms and this will be something for you to negotiate
        with your bank manager.

        iii. There is no open top version. As your horticultural
        colleagues would readily accept when driving through
        a noxious environment (whether it is nuclear fallout or
        malathion dust) it is better to be inside the vehicle
        than outside. It is possible to stand on the turret
        to take the sun but only if you have someone at the
        front end doing the driving.

        iv. Finally, as far as colour is concerned, I am
        surprised that you would want anything other than
        camouflage green. Colour is clearly customer choice
        but I would have thought that if you were operating
        the vehicle in an essentially rural environment then
        having the appearance of a cricket pitch or a laurel
        or privet hedge would be a positive advantage.

        With best wishes.

                        Yours Sincerely,

                        Peter McLoughlin

defence, showing me an article in one of the Sunday magazines about the United States F–111 aircraft. The technical data, in between the advertisements for after dinner mints and ski-ing holidays, does look very impressive. Roger has taken to calling his plan an 'upgrading of technological factors scenario', something that brought a blank look to Mr Bridger's face. The problem is, as usual, finance, and we still have not received help from the federal government in Washington. With this sort of delay it's not surprising the City of New York nearly went bankrupt. I am committed to the acquisition of a Challenger and I do not think the budget, even with a very successful Bring and Buy Sale, could stretch to the purchase of an F–111. It could be, I suppose, that the U.S.A.F. have an old one going cheap. Or, more realistically, they might be willing to hire one to us on an hourly basis. On the question of a pilot, Roger is very keen to have a go himself. I do recall a piece on *Tomorrow's World* in which an R.A.F. type said that, with all the sophisticated technology available in fighter air-craft these days, an idiot could fly them, and Roger is certainly not that. He passed his driving test at the first attempt after only six lessons in a Morris Minor. It seems that most of the flying done by fighter aircraft is at low level to avoid radar detection. It would seem good economics in our case, there-fore, if our F–111 could be adapted to spray the vegetable patch whilst on exercise. I shall write to the Commanding Officer at the U.S.A.F. base, Lakenheath, to see if such a modification is possible.

Tuesday, 19 April

A disappointing reply from the Atomic Weapons Research Establishment at Aldermaston, about converting our micro-wave oven to a missile deflector. They say they are unable to give any assurance that it would be effective. If they can't give any assurance, who can? Still, I shall let Roger loose with the screwdriver; we don't use the oven much anyway, and it will soon be the season for salad. Today I have drawn up, with

FROM: D C GORING, CHIEF ADMINISTRATIVE OFFICER
PROCUREMENT EXECUTIVE, MINISTRY OF DEFENCE

ATOMIC WEAPONS RESEARCH ESTABLISHMENT
Building F6.1

Aldermaston, Reading, RG7 4PR
Telephone Tadley 4111 (STD 073 56 4111)
Telex 848104/5

Ext: 6347
Our Ref:
Your Ref:
Date: 11 April 1983

Mr W Morgan Petty
3 Cherry Drive
Canterbury
KENT

Dear Mr Petty

Your letter of 31 March 1983 concerning the
adaption of a micro-wave oven has been referred
to me. I am, however, unable to give any assurance
that a modified oven would be effective in the role
you describe.

Yours sincerely

Roger's help, a list of people we are going to approach for items for the White Elephant Stall. Fund-raising has grown more urgent since we decided to have the Challenger modified to double as a hedge-trimmer. Top of my list is Winston Churchill, M.P., who was a junior minister at the Department of Defence until some time recently. Roger says he's not too keen on non-nuclear defence, but he will no doubt applaud our 'bulldog' spirit and sort out some little item from his wardrobe. Maybe he will have a memento associated with his grandfather – a siren suit, or one of those long cigars.

Thursday, 21 April

Good news. It seems that a group called 'Defence Begins at Home' has been set up. Roger tells me that one of its sponsors is Admiral of the Fleet Lord Hill-Norton. I write straight away, as this sounds just like the sort of organization we should contact. The pamphlet Roger has says that it seeks to encourage volunteers, lightly armed and with an intimate knowledge of the area, to help in defence work. Certainly we are both volunteers, worth a hundred pressed men, lightly armed and with an intimate knowledge of the area. I would go so far as to say that Roger knows every shrub and flower from the privet hedge in the front garden to the laurel in the rear. I have indicated to Lord Hill-Norton that I do not think it would be in either of our interests for our organizations to join together, but rather cooperate when circumstances dictate. (Swapping intelligence about gas board men who might turn out to be Russian spies, etc.) It may even be that, should we be successful in our negotiations to purchase a Challenger tank or a secondhand F–111 aircraft, his organization might like to borrow them when we're not using them.

Saturday, 23 April

A letter from the British Museum, and what is more a positive response. They suggest an Egyptian piece rather than a

THE BRITISH MUSEUM
LONDON WC1B 3DG

14 April 1983

Mr W Morgan Petty
3 Cherry Drive
Canterbury
Kent

Our ref: D/D

Dear Sir

I thank you for your letter of 10 March, which has now come to me, and for the consideration you have afforded the British Museum in formulating your future plans.

The view here is that it is not timely to discuss practical details, although you will realise that a number of insuperable formalities would inevitably arise. A few preliminary observations may not come amiss, however:

I wonder whether you have considered accommodating any material other than Roman. The arrangement with the magnolia trees sounds very tasteful, but if you also had, say, a rockery, it would at least be possible to contemplate incorporating an Egyptian piece, if Roger were willing to earmark a space of about 1 cubic yard. (Tackle would be needed if it were a major piece.)

We do not have any Roman statue that fits your description; our material is on the whole entire and of very good quality. It is not impossible, however, that there is something suitable for preservation that could enchance No. 3 Cherry Drive, and also benefit Nos 1 and 5, depending on the height of the fences and the way the numbers run.

Would you please note that I shall not be advising that any mummies or obvious funerary furniture be accommodated. Any such material in either your back or front garden could give rise to unease among the local populace, not to mention the police, and might lead to your premises being subjected to inconvenient forensic attention.

I remain, Sir,
your obedient and
grateful servant,

W. Morgan Petty, Esq.,
3 Cherry Drive,
Canterbury,
Kent.   22nd April, 1983

Dear Mr Morgan Petty,

    I get between ten and twenty letters a day, nearly all of which are either boring or hard work or both, and hardly ever one which I enjoy. Yours was, accordingly, a great pleasure to read. I am replying at once, though I cannot afford Recorded Delivery.

    I am excited to think that one corner of a Kentish field is stoutly defended. I have a scythe with a curved steel blade about four feet long, if you or Roger feel that this would usefully thicken up your defences. If you are not accustomed to their use you can quite suddenly become about nine inches shorter, usually in the non-master leg.

    You will have an exciting time in your Challenger, which normally has a crew of four, but I dare say that if you were to lash the tiller and put a suitable weight on the accelerator one of you could traverse the gun while the other loads and fires it.

    I wish you the best of British.

Yours sincerely,

Hill-Norton.

Roman one, covering about a cubic yard. I have discussed their proposals with Roger and am surprised to learn that the subject of Egyptian relics is not totally foreign to him. It appears that he once ordered a book from the library on tomatoes and, through an error in the index, received one on tombs instead. This volume was his reading matter throughout the wet spring of 1974. He has asked that I inform the British Museum of his stated preference for the Sixth Dynasty, from King Teti through the reigns of Pepi I and his half-brother Pepi II. I also ask them to refrain from sending anything of a sexually explicit nature, as Mr Bridger was outraged by the partial nudity in the recent B.B.C. series *The Cleopatras* and, as a member of the Festival of Light, would take exception to anything too racy.

Monday, 25 April

A reply arrives from Lord Hill-Norton. The efficiency of these military men is a constant source of wonderment to me. Not only efficient, but with an offer of further military hardware – a scythe with a curved steel blade four foot long. Roger is cock-a-hoop. Not only will it help defend our borders but also clear out an awkward corner of couch grass near the strawberries.

Tuesday, 26 April

A note from Winston Churchill M.P. That was quick. I wonder if he too is a military man. I was expecting a package with his donation but when I saw the envelope I thought a cheque would do just as well. Unfortunately, he has sent neither, but suggests that we safeguard our peace and freedom by playing a full part in NATO. I must say Roger and I had not thought of that. If we joined NATO, we might get a few perks – discount on equipment, etc. I shall write at once to Dr Josef Luns who runs it, asking for a brochure for potential members and an application form.

WINSTON S. CHURCHILL, M.P.

HOUSE OF COMMONS
LONDON SW1A OAA

01-219 3405

22 April 1983

Dear Mr Morgan Petty

Very many thanks for your letter of 16
April.

While I admire your redoubtable 'bulldog'
spirit towards national defence and wish you
well, I am bound to say that the only realistic
way of safe-guarding our peace and freedom is
by strengthening our defences on a national
scale and continuing to play our full part in
NATO while maintaining our independent nuclear
deterrent.

With best wishes.

Yours sincerely

W Morgan Petty Esq
3 Cherry Drive
Canterbury
Kent

DAILY EXPRESS   Express
Newspapers
Limited

121 Fleet Street
London EC4P 4JT
Telephone
01-353 8000
Telex No 21841
Cable Address
Express London

27th April, 1983

Mr. W. Morgan Petty,
3 Cherry Drive,
Canterbury,
Kent.

Dear Mr. Petty,

Thank you for your most amusing and
interesting letter.

Best wishes.

Yours sincerely,

MAX HASTINGS

MH/AG

Registered in London No 141748.
Registered office: 121 Fleet St London EC4P 4JT

**Manpower
Services Commission**

Selkirk House
166 High Holborn
London WC1V 6PF
Telephone: 01-836 6126

Chairman: David Young

Your ref:

Our ref:

Date: 18 April, 1983

W. Morgan Petty, Esq.,
3 Cherry Drive,
Canterbury,
Kent.

Dear Mr. Petty,

My Chairman, David Young, has asked me to thank you
for your most enlightening letter of 26th March.

Although the content of your letter is primarily the
concern of the Ministry of Defence, I understand from the
last paragraph that you require the services of two individuals
to defend your sovereign territory.

The only scheme administered by the Manpower Services
Commission which could be of any help to you is the Youth
Training Scheme which is intended to provide one year's
foundation training for school leavers. I am, therefore,
enclosing a leaflet describing the scheme in more detail.

I hope this is helpful.

yours sincerely

David Vere

David Vere
Private Secretary

Thursday, 28 April

I receive a letter from Max Hastings in reply to my request for a little something for the Bring and Buy. For some reason he calls my letter 'most amusing', although I fail to see anything amusing about trying to protect one's borders. Perhaps Mr Hastings's secretary has made a mistake; I shall write again. A more productive letter in the second post from the Manpower Services Commission. They say that the only way in which they could help us is through the Youth Training Scheme. I was hoping for battle-hardened veterans, but it might be that we will have to make do with a couple of unemployed Boy Scouts. Roger has been working on the microwave oven missile deflector for nearly a week now. This evening, with further modifications carried out, he plugged it into the electric socket in the shed. I am not sure whether it was wise of him to stay inside after it glowed red, but I think he has recovered from the noise of the explosion now that he has had a glass of brandy and hot water.

Friday, 29 April

I have sent an update on our position here to Mr Heseltine. I can only assume that his full reply to my earlier letter has gone astray in the post. I am able to confirm that any earlier misgivings I had about awakening to the clatter of AK 47s against a background chorus of 'The Volga Boatmen' have receded. However, I also have to tell him the bad news that, since Roger broke his penknife trying to mend (once again) the second of our garden forks, he has finally given it up as a bad job. I know how passionately Mr Heseltine says he is committed to the cause of defence, and so I ask for a little something for our White Elephant Stall. Roger says he thinks the Secretary of State is quite rich and that I should also ask for a donation of twenty pounds, an amount sufficient to buy a new garden fork. I have every confidence Mr Heseltine will oblige.

Saturday, 30 April

Operation Tulip begins, so called because it begins behind the tulip bed and is designed to test our 'Rapid Deployment Force', Roger, on roller-skates, seeing how fast he can get from there to the pond and thus prevent a bridgehead being secured by the water lilies. Not on reflection a good idea. The exercise started off very well, but at Roger's suggestion we built a bonfire covered in wet rags near the battle. The aim was to simulate smoke from a barrage blowing across the garden path. Unfortunately the smoke was so dense that Roger misjudged the distance to the pond and, unable to stop his skates, fell in. Once again the carp show no sign of damage, but a soaking in the icy cold water has lowered Roger's morale. Of course, in a war situation, morale is a critical element, and I have decided to maintain ours by means of our very own battle song. I remember in the film *Zulu*, Cy Endfield's tribute to the defenders of Rorke's Drift, there was a scene where Ivor Emmanuel led the remaining soldiers in a chorus of 'Men of Harlech' – something which at the time made a strong impression on me. Roger has a very nice baritone voice and, facing the hordes that any potential enemy might send against us, something of our own to sing would lift our spirits. (Why should the Devil have all the best tunes?) I shall approach Sir Michael Tippett, whose work I greatly admire, to see if he can find time to compose a short, rousing song, in two-part harmony, that Roger and I might use in our defence.

Tuesday, 3 May

At last a letter from the Ministry of Agriculture. I had hoped this would settle the dispute between Roger and Mr Bridger. Although neither has mentioned the incident of some weeks ago, I have no doubt that the tension over who is right about the effects of 'fall-out' lies just under the surface waiting to erupt. Despite the letter's length, I am not much wiser for reading it. Worst hit, it appears, would be cauliflowers and

Ministry of Agriculture, Fisheries and Food
Whitehall Place London S.W.1A 2HH

Telex 889351

Direct line 01
Switchboard 01-

Mr W Morgan Petty
3 Cherry Drive
Canterbury
Kent

Your reference

Our reference   DEF 638

Date   28 April 1983

Dear Mr Morgan Petty

I have been asked to reply on behalf of the Minister to your letter of 11 March.

Before dealing with the effects of radioactive fallout on foodstuffs I will attempt to describe 'fallout' itself as you requested.

An explosion of any kind, when detonated at or near the surface of the earth, causes soil and other material to be thrown or drawn up into a column of hot, rising gases and to be carried aloft. In a nuclear explosion the radioactive elements, produced by the explosion and vaporised by heat, condense into or on the material drawn into the rising gases. Soil is the major component of this surface material, great amounts of which rise many thousands of feet into the air before the particles begin to fall back again due to gravitational pull. The amount of material involved in this process is of course directly proportional to the size of the nuclear device.

The larger particles would fall rapidly but the lighter 'fine sand' particles would be carried in the wind and would fall, appreciably later, many miles - even hundreds of miles - away from the point of detonation. Owing to the variations in weapon yield, wind and other factors it is impossible to predict the nature or extent of fall-out particles. Detailed advice would be available at the time on areas affected and the period of radioactive danger based on the particular decay rate of the particles concerned. These radioactive particles would be harmful if ingested or allowed to come into contact with the skin and thus it would be essential for food to be examined and elementary precautions taken before preparing it for consumption.

The 'sand-like' fall out particles would not be removed by boiling or cooking and would need to be removed beforehand. Stored food would be safe to eat provided it was in sealed containers or otherwise protected so that fallout dust could not settle on the food itself. Similarly fully grown vegetables protected by a pod or skin, such as peas and potatoes, would be safe to eat provided that they were first washed (to remove any fallout dust) and then shelled or peeled in the usual way. Immature growing plants, on the otherhand, would be best avoided lest they had taken up radioactivity from the soil through their root systems.

Green vegetables would be a little more difficult on which to generalise for whilst a 'hard' cabbage or firm hearted lettuce could be rendered edible by removal of the outer leaves and thorough washing, cauliflower or broccoli with its irregular configuration would be extremely difficult to wash free of particles.   Rubber gloves should, of course, be worn when handling prior and during washing items likely to be contaminated.   The same principle applies to other foodstuffs and more detailed information would be made readily available if the threat of an attack appeared likely.

You will appreciate from the above information that fallout has more far-reaching effects than the greenfly which troubled Roger in 1974.   The one similarity is that both its and their effect can be minimised by the use of water - aided, in the case pf greenfly, by the addition of a little soap solution.

I trust you will find this information and the enclosed leaflets helpful, although I am afraid the latter deal only with the more common problems encountered rather than with the rather less likely one of fallout.

Yours sincerely

P G ALLIX

broccoli, and the writer does say that the effects would be more far-reaching than those of the greenfly in 1974. Thus, whilst it doesn't confirm Mr Bridger's view about discolouring soft fruit, it does appear that his assessment of 'fall-out' is nearer the mark. On the other hand, the last thing I want is Roger going into one of his sulks with so much to do. I think that in this instance I shall keep the contents of this letter to myself.

Thursday, 5 May

A bad day. I am afraid that Roger and myself have had words. I casually mentioned that as we had not had a reply from the U.S.A.F. to our letter concerning the possible hire of an F–111 aircraft, given our other commitments we should abandon the idea for the time being. I now realize my mistake; with the pigeons having attacked his early peas (we used the netting to camouflage the slit trench), Roger was in no mood to suffer another disappointment. I had no idea his desire to be a fighter pilot was so strong. Perhaps I should have been warned by the small silk scarf he took to wearing after seeing that film about Douglas Bader. In the event, I hurriedly withdrew the suggestion and agreed instead to ask British Aerospace how much a Hawker Harrier costs to buy. I suppose the Harrier does have the advantage of vertical take-off, and we could thus do without the tedious business of building a runway, something that would involve moving the gladioli. Heaven knows how we'll pay for it. Perhaps they will give us a discount for buying British.

Friday, 6 May

In the Command Bunker/dining room, here at Cherry Drive, I am reading Erwin Rommel's book on tank warfare, and deciding how to make best use of our Challenger, when Mr Oliver arrives. He says he has something wrong with his motorized winding system, whatever that may be, and could Roger help him mend it. I explain that Roger is at the doctor's having the dressing on his boil changed, and Mr Oliver then remarks that he hopes he'll be fit for the 15th. It seems they have agreed to go together to the judging of a Camera Club competition called 'Snapping in the Spring'. The last thing in the world I want to do is inhibit Roger's creative activities, but I have to point out to Mr Oliver that the 15th is also the date for Operation Foxglove to begin. It is vitally important that this goes all right because it is our audition piece if the NATO generals want to see us in action before letting us join. I sense that Mr Oliver is not pleased, and even less so when I tell him we have still not found the missing piece of his Yashica. At 13.40 military time there is tremendous interference on the portable radio. With manoeuvres at night we have taken to listening to the repeat broadcasts of *The Archers* in the afternoon. This disruption greatly annoys Roger, who I know is very worried about the Grundys. Given his very agitated state I wonder about the psychological impact the loss of Radio Four, during a period of crisis, would have on him. What's more, I understand from Roger that the U.S.A.F. intends stationing EF–111A aircraft at Upper Heyford somewhere in Oxfordshire. Although neither of us understands all the technicalities of this new aeroplane, from what Roger has read, its purpose seems to be to jam communications prior to an attack by other U.S. aircraft. I must confess that I find this a little strange, as I have always understood that American nuclear weapons were for defence only and, if you've been attacked, you would not need to jam communications as the enemy would undoubtedly expect retaliation. Still, I am sure there is an explanation that would not occur to simple souls like us. What I am very concerned about, however, is the effect these EF–111A aircraft's jamming may have on Radio Four. Both Roger and myself are regular listeners and, especially at a time when the world beyond our boundaries is a mass of blackened, smoking rubble, I am sure that we would find it a huge comfort. I shall drop a line to the U.S.A.F. at Upper Heyford and ask them if, as well as blacking out Soviet radar, it will interfere with *Gardeners' Question Time* or *The Archers* and, if they do have to retaliate (or dare I suggest strike first), could they please avoid doing it on Sundays between 2.00 and 2.30 p.m., or weekdays between 7.05 and 7.20 p.m. To be on the safe side, in case I miss an episode of *The Archers*, I shall also ask them to avoid the omnibus edition, Sundays, 10.15–11.15 a.m.

Saturday, 7 May

Last week I settled down with Roger to watch a programme narrated by Ludovic Kennedy, called *A Guide to Armageddon*. I must confess that neither Roger nor myself had any idea where Armageddon was, and we couldn't find it in the atlas. Roger said he thought it was one of the Greek islands. Imagine our shock when we settled back with our cocoa, expecting to hear Mr Kennedy take us on an exploration of Hellenic glories, only to find ourselves watching St Paul's Cathedral being blown up by a one-megaton bomb and assorted couples trying to live in makeshift shelters. Whilst I anticipate that, in the event of a thermonuclear conflagration, we shall remain safe behind our privet hedges, this television programme has raised the question of what we shall do for water and sewerage services if the area outside our zone, which we rely on for their provision, is destroyed? Curtailment could present us with a hygiene problem. I am already concerned about the effects of Mr Bridger's gift of manure, which Roger has left piled near the greenhouse. If we had to suffer a similar odour for any length of time after a nuclear attack, it would be most distressing. Roger suggests I drop a note to Tom King, who is the Secretary of State in charge of sewage at the Department of the Environment. I just hope he replies soon. This is urgent.

Monday, 9 May

A reply from Sir Austin Pearce, the Chairman of British Aerospace. He thinks the down-thrust of the Harrier's exhaust would damage the gladioli and the paintwork on the house,

49

British Aerospace
PUBLIC LIMITED COMPANY

From the Chairman,
SIR AUSTIN PEARCE, CBE

100 Pall Mall
London SW1Y 5HR

Telephone: 01-930 1020
Telegrams: Britair London
Telex: 24353

Mr. W. Morgan Petty,
3, Cherry Drive,
Canterbury,
Kent.   3rd May, 1983.

     Thank you for your letter of the 23rd
April, which I have seen today on the subject
of your decision and your interest in the
purchase of a Harrier.

     Clearly, any prices which might be
quoted would vary considerably depending upon
the electronic and weapons fit which you put
on the aircraft, and the release of such equipment would be heavily dependent upon the views
of the Ministry of Defence. There is, however,
a more serious problem with the Harrier, which
is that due to the down-thrust of the jet exhaust
which comes out at a very high temperature, anything beneath it is subject to very high temperatures,
and I am afraid this would mean your gladioli and
other living matter would suffer very severely,
in addition to which the paintwork on your house
would not be improved if you were at all close to
the take-off area. So if you wish to preserve the
appearance of your garden, and this would appear
to be one of your requirements, then quite frankly
I do not believe the Harrier is the right piece
of equipment.

        Yours sincerely,

and for that reason a purchase by ourselves would be a non-starter. It was nice of him to be concerned, but Roger will not be too happy to have his plans for soaring up amongst the clouds thwarted again.

Tuesday, 10 May

I have spent the day on more letters soliciting items for the 'Challenger for Cherry Drive' Bring and Buy Sale. I have approached H.R.H. Prince Philip, as I am sure that around the Palace there are a great number of objects, gifts from Middle East potentates or heads of countries nobody's ever heard of, that he would like to see the back of. If this is the case, then, given their royal associations, I am sure they would be snapped up. I have also approached Mr Michael Foot, the leader of the Labour Party. I have noticed that in the newspapers, and on television, he has been looking very well turned out of late, almost elegant. Both Roger and myself were wondering what he had done with the old clothes that were so very much a feature of his public appearances. If he is not keeping them for the garden, and is not sure what to do with them, perhaps he would consider donating a suit or two to us to help us raise money for our tank. The second post brings a reply to a similar request I made to Dr David Owen. Neither Roger nor myself (nor, I suspect, many other people) has any idea what the S.D.P./Liberal Alliance's policy on defence is. Roger did say that he had seen Dr Owen on *Question Time* once and, from what he said then, he's fairly sure he's in favour of conventional military responses. I remember Mr Oliver, who wears coloured shirts and is a chartered accountant, saying that the S.D.P. were the bright dynamic party of the future. Such a shame, then, that Dr Owen forgot to enclose the summary of their White Paper on defence. I feel sure this would be snapped up as a curio at our forthcoming Bring and Buy.

From: The Rt Hon Dr David Owen MP

HOUSE OF COMMONS
LONDON SWIA OAA

3 May 1983

W Morgan Petty Esq
3 Cherry Drive
Canterbury
Kent

Dear Mr Petty

Thank you for your letter. I am enclosing
for your information a summary of the SDP White
Paper on Defence and Disarmament which I hope
will help to explain our policies in this
important area.

Yours sincerely

David Owen

Wednesday, 11 May

Roger very down. He has told Mr Oliver that he cannot go to the Camera Club on the 15th, and they have had words. I heard Mr Oliver shouting something about 'being let down' just before a door slammed and a car drove off at speed. I think the position has been made worse by his having sent his Yashica back to the manufacturers to replace the missing part, and being told it is a discontinued line. I tried to cheer Roger up by saying that I did not think his picture of 'Forsythia in Bud' would have won the competition anyway. In response, he banged the shed closed and turned the volume on Radio Four full up. I was hoping to get Roger to draft a letter, in American, to William Casey, who is the Director of the Central Intelligence Agency. On *World in Action* (or was it *Panorama?*) there was an item about 'The Company', as I understand it is called, having huge stockpiles of captured Russian arms around the world, which they use to discredit governments, and as a pretext to invade them. If these stockpiles are so large, they surely wouldn't miss a couple of R.P.G. launchers or bazookas. I tell them that we are involved in a 'projected capability force analysis'. It is possible that The Company might perceive our non-nuclear stance as the first step towards pacifism. But I assure them I hold my freedom and the integrity of my land, with its traditions of cream teas and the sound of willow on leather, just as dear as their own countrymen hold their cultural heritage of hamburgers and episodes of *Dallas*. Projected capability force analysis? The American language is not so difficult once you get the hang of it.

Thursday, 12 May

A loud cry causes me to rush outside. Roger has trapped another man in the half-dug anti-tank ditch and is standing guard over him. I thought he had discovered a spy and thus taken our first prisoner of war. However, it turns out that he was a pigeon fancier looking for his lost champion Blue Danzig. I point out sternly that he is in a restricted military zone and ask Roger to escort him from the area. He looks at us very oddly and mutters something under his breath. When Roger returns he explains that the confusion arose from his not knowing quite what a Russian looks like. We know what Americans look like. A very nice man called Hank, who came from Seattle, used to give talks on cross-pollination at the Gardening Society, but we are not sure of being able to recognize a Russian, neither of us having met one. There have, of course, been pictures on television, but we all know how deceptive they can be. (I remember how terribly upset Roger was after seeing Michael Parkinson in the flesh.) From the stuff they write in the *Daily Mail*, I imagine them to be seven foot tall, constantly drunk on vodka, and with an insatiable appetite for violating young Englishwomen, but surely they can't all be like that. Roger tells me that a Malcolm Rifkind, someone quite junior at the Foreign and Commonwealth Office, has just returned from a visit to the Soviet Union, and so doubtless he will have met some first hand. I shall drop him a line to see if he can enlighten us as to their appearance and, maybe if he has one, he could let us have a snapshot. Then if we do find any suspicious characters lurking near the lupins, we shall know how to tell if they are Russian.

Friday, 13 May

There has been a lot of innuendo of late, mostly by Mr Heseltine, to the effect that Nuclear Free Zones do not enjoy popular support. I think that is a little arrogant of him, as he has not once visited us here to see how clearly Roger and I are committed to non-nuclear defence. Politicians really ought to be more careful of their generalizations. However, such allegations may affect our dealings with other bodies in this country and abroad. So that this is cleared up once and for all, I shall hold a referendum on the matter. The electoral roll would consist of myself and Roger, who, whilst he is not actually resident, spends his days in the garden and his nights on sentry duty. I have therefore for this purpose awarded him resident status. I will act as polling clerk while Roger votes, and he will act as polling clerk while I vote. I am hoping to persuade Mr Bridger to act as returning officer. So that there can be no allegations of 'ballot rigging' I shall approach the Electoral Reform Society, who (Roger tells me) do all the most important elections and are completely trustworthy, to ask if they will count the votes. It should not be a very strenuous task, even with a number of re-counts. Looking at our cash balance figure, one pound, thirty-five pence, I just hope they do not charge too much.

Saturday, 14 May

I have made an historic decision. Roger and I will build our own multi-role combat aircraft. I have even thought of a name for it: 'The Squirrel'. I admit that this is not the most warlike of names, but I understand that, if cornered, a squirrel can give you a very nasty nip from its nut-piercing teeth. It is an idea I have had in mind ever since Sir Austin Pearce explained the Harrier's drawbacks to me and the reply to my letter to the U.S.A.F. got lost in the post. I have not mentioned the idea to Roger as, if it does not come off, I would not like the failure to compound his earlier disappointments. I shall consult Lucas Aerospace on the design once we have sorted out the multi-roles that we would want the Squirrel to undertake – bombing and strafing of enemy contingents and a little bit of low-level garden spraying; then they might be able to help prepare plans from which Roger could work. In the light of British Aerospace's comments, we shall not attempt a vertical take-off capacity, but design for short take-off in some eighty feet (the length of the back garden). I realize that they might think that we are being ambitious, but I did explain how good Roger is with mechanical things, citing as examples of his prowess the way in which he fixed the motor mower and how expertly he wired the greenhouse. Two other considerations have had to be given to production of the prototype. The first is materials. Roger tells me that the British Steel Corporation have recently acquired a new Chairman, an Anglo-American called Ian MacGregor. Apparently Mr MacGregor emigrated to the United States to seek his fortune. I suppose the fact that he has come back means he had no luck. I wonder when that was exactly? If it was before the 1939–45 war, he will not remember everybody searching out their saucepans and taking down their railings to make Spitfires. It was my intention to obtain the materials for the Squirrel in the same way. I have made an inventory of the scrap available to us – an old fork-head, a wheelbarrow with a broken handle, sundry hinges and bits of wire mesh – but, even with all of this and the two buckets with the bottoms rusted out that Mr Bridger gave us, I think we would be hard pressed to make a wing. I shall therefore contact Mr MacGregor, who Roger says is anxious to get rid of a large stockpile of steel, to see if he can sell us enough for the fuselage and the other wing. Maybe, if we offer to collect it, they will give us a discount. Labour, happily, should not present a problem. By coincidence I saw, on the television news, film of a group of school-leavers in the North East who had, assisted by a government scheme, built a light aircraft. I would therefore imagine that we could benefit under a similar scheme. I do not think the building of a subsonic, low-level fighter bomber should prove any more difficult than the construction of the piston-driven monoplane built by the youngsters in the North East. That nice David Young at the Manpower Services Commission will no doubt be able to rustle up a dozen or so eager young apprentices to help Roger.

Sunday, 15 May

Operation Foxglove. Roger is on parade at 6.00 a.m. After inspection (I have to reprimand him for a dirty garden fork) and a spot of weeding, we set about preparing our position. Roger is anxious to use his newly made baked-bean-tin bomb.

Just as we are ready to start, two visitors appear at the front door. They are, they inform me, from the Church of Jesus Christ and the Latter Day Saints. I must admit they have funny accents, which appear to come from somewhere between the Bronx and Middlesbrough, but still they are smartly dressed and do not appear to be selling anything. I am just about to offer them a cup of coffee when there is a small explosion down by the shrubbery. We find Roger lying some-what dazed and blackened amongst the delphiniums. There are obviously still problems on the fusing of the baked-bean-tin bomb. The young men helped me carry Roger into the house. This, I now realize, was a mistake, as they soon struck up a strong affinity, and the three of them spent the afternoon discussing basketball. Roger's knowledge of this subject seemed encyclopedic. He really does amaze me sometimes. When our religious friends have gone, Roger leaves to stand sentry. Such a pity it has started to rain so heavily, and such a pity about Operation Foxglove.

Tuesday, 17 May

Roger has a very heavy cold and is in very low spirits. Some-thing not helped by Mr Oliver, who turns up in an orange shirt and tells us that his picture 'Robin Redbreast's Dinner' won the first prize in the Camera Club competition. I think he showed us that one, and I can't say I remember being im-pressed. The second post brings a letter from David Crouch, the Member of Parliament for Canterbury. It seems that our letter to the Treasury has been passed to him, Nigel Lawson having moved on. I do wish Mrs Thatcher would stop swap-ping her ministers about, it does confuse things so, and in practical terms they've probably only just learned the job before they're gone. Mr Crouch's letter does little to dispel the gloom here at Cherry Drive. Still, I am glad we have made contact with him, as when we take delivery of the Challenger, it will be expensive to run this as well as the Morris Minor and the latter will probably have to go. In the circumstances we

From: David Crouch, M.P.

HOUSE OF COMMONS
LONDON SWIA OAA

May 11,1983

Dear Mr. Petty,

Your letter dated March 22nd and addressed to
Mr.Nigel Lawson at the Treasury has been passed to me.
Mr.Lawson, who was formerly in the Treasury, has for over
a year been Secretary of State for Energy.

Having read your letter I wondered whether you
were being wholly serious. I can appreciate your sincere
concern at the prospect of nuclear was which,I,along with
every sane person would share. Conservative Government policy
on defence is to prevent war breaking out and to aim at
multilateral nuclear disarmament.

I am enclosing a note I prepared on this subject
for your information.

Yours sincerely,

David Crouch.

W. Morgan Petty, Esq.,
3, Cherry Drive,
Canterbury, Kent.

will have to do the shopping in the Challenger. I must admit I am not exactly sure how big this tank is, but I do foresee problems getting it around some of the smaller shopping precincts, and I anticipate terrible trouble at the new St Dunstan's mini-roundabout. I shall prevail upon Mr Crouch to point out to the City Council the important nature of my defence work. I shall also ask him, in the event that we cannot get anyone famous, if he would be prepared to cut the ribbon and generally declare the 'Challenger for Cherry Drive' Bring and Buy Sale open.

Thursday, 19 May

Roger has gone to visit Mr Bridger in hospital. Mr Bridger has done something to his back whilst digging and has asked Roger to 'keep an eye' on his garden as well as ours while he is laid up. Reluctantly, I have agreed that he can. It has been our policy since our nuclear free declaration to be very close to the zone at all times. Then if hostility does break out suddenly, we can nip smartly into our garden for protection. In Mr Bridger's garden, Roger will be almost ten minutes away even if he runs. Perhaps we could give the Ministry of Defence our telephone number and they could warn us a little earlier than everyone else, then Roger could set off from Mr Bridger's before the streets are full of panicking people. Better still, maybe we could persuade Mr Bridger to declare his bungalow and garden a Nuclear Free Zone. On this last question Roger has informed me that we are not the only such designated area. He has seen a picture in the *Guardian* of a road sign which declares Greater Manchester a Nuclear Free Zone. I discovered that the Greater London Council, whose leader is that nice young man who brought down the bus fares, was also nuclear free. I would like to think that we could take the entire credit by having set the example, but I suppose it is just possible that others have come to an anti-nuclear conclusion separately. I wonder if they have had the same lack of helpful response from central government that we have encountered, although I suppose Mr Heseltine's replies to both of our letters could have gone astray in the post. It occurs to me that if there are such Nuclear Free Zones elsewhere in the country perhaps we could discuss 'twinning', leading to a cultural exchange. I understand from Roger that they have a very fine orchestra in Manchester, the Hallé. Maybe they would like to come and play here; we could reciprocate with a rendition of the new Cherry Drive battle song which we hope Sir Michael Tippett will compose for us. I shall make inquiries straight away.

Friday, 20 May

Roger has been trying to patch his corduroy trousers. Personally, I think they have given up the ghost, the final straw coming when he fell into a heap of manure backing out of the greenhouse. The vigorous washing needed to rid them of the odour was such that the cotton gave way. I have been thinking a great deal of late about our dress. In a small military unit like our own, turnout is vitally important, and I have to admit that our current apparel is a little haphazard – Roger in his now irreparable corduroy trousers, combat jacket and red and white balaclava, and myself in cavalry twill, hacking jacket and felt hat. I think it would be very good for morale if we were to have our own specially designed uniform, both combat and dress. I did mention to Letitia Odette (who dropped in, much to Roger's annoyance, to borrow a garden rake) what I had in mind, and she kindly offered to run these up for us. However, I still have the pullover she knitted as a present for Christmas of 1978. On that occasion there was some confusion over sizes, and it turned out three times too big and with only one sleeve. As it will be necessary for military efficiency that these uniforms be cut to perfection, I asked Roger (he keeps abreast of the fashion world) who were the most exciting of the young designers. After all, efficiency doesn't dictate that we have to be unfashionable. He tells me of a David and Elizabeth Emmanuel, and I drop them a line asking for a price for two uniforms each, with shorts for the summer. On the question of material and colour, the former will have to be lightweight so that in emergencies we can don our anti-gas equipment quickly, and not coarse-grained, as Roger has a very sensitive skin. We anticipate taking delivery of our Challenger, which we have now firmly decided we would like in maroon, and so the colour should be something that would not clash with that. Roger told me that there was a slump in the textile industry and so I am sure Mr and Mrs Emmanuel will be grateful for the work.

Sunday, 22 May

More gloom on the financial front. There are now just two pounds in the Defence Fund, and Roger will want most of this for seeds. Despite Mr Bridger paying Roger ten pounds for the help he gave him and a further ten pounds for next week, until he is back on his feet again, we are still on somewhat shaky fiscal ground. What I think we need is some sort of subsidy from those financially better placed supporters of peace. I was just basting the roast chicken when the thought hit me. The Nobel Prize. Now, if we could win that, it would really solve our cash-flow problem. We have declared ourselves nuclear free and tried to encourage other people to renounce the stockpiling and use of nuclear weapons. (I am sure we have persuaded Mr Bridger of the rationality of this cause, and it is only a matter of time before he follows our example.) Furthermore, a little while ago I wrote to Mr Richard Adelman offering Roger's logistical support for his arms limitation talks in Geneva. (Making the tea, laying the table, babysitting, taking the delegates' dogs for walks.) With a track record like this, we should stand an excellent chance of winning. After all, Roger says they gave a Peace Prize to Henry Kissinger, who bombed North Vietnam flat. What I have to establish now is how we go about being nominated for the Nobel Peace Prize. Can anyone nominate anyone else? If so, perhaps Roger and I could nominate each other, giving us two chances. I must admit, I am not really sure exactly how much this prize is currently worth, but after a small reward for all our hard work (Roger would like a new rotovator and I would welcome a boxed set of the works of Stravinsky) I'm sure there should be a good bit left over to go into our Defence Fund.

Monday, 23 May

Today we do our P.T. at the usual time, eight o'clock. Having the best equipment will not be enough if Roger and I are not fit. We do ten minutes of something Roger calls 'aerobics' to a record by Angela Rippon, who I recall as the very pretty girl who used to read the news on B.B.C. television. It's such a shame to see her reduced to teaching P.T. Normally we have our physical jerks inside but, since Roger's rather energetic overarm knocked the barometer off the living-room wall, we only do our 'aerobics' inside when the weather's bad. Roger has a very chesty cough, the result of last week's exercise simulating a night attack down by the compost heap. He played the role of a crack Soviet division, and, trying hard to outflank me, he walked right past my position – a testament, I think, to my camouflage. I stepped out to make this point but, startled by the sound of a voice behind him, he over-balanced and tumbled into the pond. What we really need is a lesson from the professionals. I bet the Parachute Regiment don't need Miss Rippon.

Wednesday, 25 May

Mr Oliver, green shirt this time, arrives just as Roger is busy in the garden, weeding. More interruptions. He tells us that his picture 'Robin Redbreast's Dinner' has been entered in the Kent Camera Club's area finals. I watch Roger gulp very hard at this news and only hope that it will not drive him into one of his sulks. Mr Oliver also tells us that Michael Hardiman and he are going to London for a conference on 'Photographic Techniques for the Gifted Amateur'. I note how pointedly he does not ask Roger. Needless to say, I get little work from him in the garden this afternoon. If I did not know Mr Oliver was a supporter of the S.D.P., I might think him a fifth-columnist whose mission was to disrupt defence work here at 3 Cherry Drive. I must say that I find his attitude to our defence work very irritating and I know it upsets Roger. However, as I pointed out, if there is a thermonuclear exchange, Roger and I will be safely tending the flower beds whilst Mr Oliver, coloured shirts and all, will be heaven knows where.

What I think we really need is an advertising campaign, and I know just the people, Saatchi and Saatchi. If we can enlist their help to mount some publicity to explain the serious nature of our position here, then the battle will be half won. (I understand that Mr Saatchi and his brother were able to present Conservative Party policies as intelligible to a great number of people, something that testifies extremely highly to their talents.) I shall ask them to model our campaign on those pictures of Winston Churchill which appeared in the last war. With a picture of Roger and myself standing in defiant pose, holding our scythe and bayonet, giving the 'V' sign under the caption: 'IF THEY DON'T NEED NUCLEAR WEAPONS – DO YOU?' I shall ask Mr Saatchi to 'run this up the flagpole' as I understand they say in the advertising world and advise us as to the cost.

Friday, 27 May

Left alone this morning (Roger had to go to the hospital to have a septic splinter removed from his finger) I glance through some back copies of the *Guardian* newspaper that Roger keeps for lining seed trays. In one of the international news sections I find a piece about Mr Paul Nitze (such an odd name) who is the United States chief negotiator at the intermediate weapons talks in Geneva. It seems there are difficulties over the inclusion of French and British weapons in the totals under discussion. Although we have no nuclear arsenal we do have a very formidable array of conventional weaponry, which we operate on Dual Key policy, the lock on the shed needing both mine and Roger's keys to open it. I wonder whether, if we offer to put some of this – say Roger's grandfather's bayonet – into the discussions in Geneva, it would overcome what the Americans call 'a log jam situation' and act as an incentive to both sides. I shall talk to Roger when he gets back and, if he agrees, drop Mr Nitze a line. Maybe he will want a fuller explanation. If so I shall send Roger to Switzerland; he is after all my second in command (inevitable, as there are only the two of us) and he could no doubt do with a break.

Saturday, 28 May

Two letters today. The first is from a major in the Parachute Regiment. He suggests that we buy a record: 'Get Fighting Fit With 2 PARA'. (Maybe they do have Angela Rippon on this as well.) I must admit to finding it all a little disillusioning. I had visions of men being trained by wiry P.T. instructors with muscles of iron. It now seems that they all get together in the barrack square and put on a seventy-eight. Still, I shall send for the record. Maybe there's a good battle song on it somewhere. The second letter is from the Royal Air Force. It seems that they have taken to answering the U.S.A.F.'s mail as well now. At least its content is encouraging and confirms that the U.S.A.F. will not under any circumstances interfere with Radio Four. I must say that's a great deal off my mind.

Monday, 30 May

Dear God. The ecclesiastical mud has certainly hit the fan today. A Roman Catholic archbishop called Bruno Heim, whose job is Apostolic Pro-Nuncio (as clear as mud to someone not of the faith), has accused those involved with unilateral nuclear disarmament of being 'useful idiots or consciously sharing Soviet aggressiveness and ideology'. Roger is of the Catholic faith, although he lapsed some time ago. But like a lot of people who were very religious in early life (I understand

From: Major B K Martin

REGIMENTAL HEADQUARTERS
THE PARACHUTE REGIMENT
BROWNING BARRACKS
ALDERSHOT, HAMPSHIRE

Tel: Army: Aldershot Military)
 Civil: (STD Code 0252   ) Ext.642
 Aldershot 24431   )

MS8

W Morgan Petty
3 Cherry Drive
CANTERBURY
Kent

23 May 1983

Dear Morgan Petty,

Thank you for your letter dated 8 May which has been passed to me.

The best advice I could give you and Roger is to buy the 2 PARA record called "Get Fighting Fit with 2 PARA". This record was made as a result of the Falklands Campaign and contains progressive exercises which give speed, skill, stamina, strength and suppleness to be ready for anything. I am sure it will meet your needs to become a crack fighting unit!

The address of 2 PARA is:

2nd Battalion
The Parachute Regiment
Brunveal Barracks
ALDERSHOT
Hants.

Yours faithfully,

B.K. Martin

ROYAL AIR FORCE
Upper Heyford Oxford OX5 3LN

Telephone: Upper Heyford (086982) 4828

W Morgan Petty
3 Cherry Drive
CANTERBURY
Kent

Please reply to
Royal Air Force Commander
Your reference

Our reference UH/351/PR

Date 24 May 1983

Dear Sir

Thank you for your letter dated 9 May 1983 in
which you discussed possible interference by the
EF-111A aircraft to be stationed at RAF Upper
Heyford. Your letter was passed to me for action
in my capacity as the Royal Air Force Liaison
Officer to the USAF at Upper Heyford.

I have been asked by the USAF authorities to
assure yourself and Roger that the USAF will not,
under any circumstances, interfere with Radio 4
or any of the programmes you mentioned.

Yours faithfully

D JENKING
Squadron Leader
RAF Commander

that he was so well thought of as a choirboy that he was allowed to swing the incense around) he has never really overcome his early indoctrination. Consequently, he has been cut to the quick by the archbishop's remarks. This, in his already depressed state, caused by a good soaking in the rain of Sunday's guard duty, has driven him into one of his sulks. I have not seen him this upset since Peter Blaker, the Armed Forces minister, made some similarly silly 'off the cuff remarks', something for which, I would add, he still has not apologized. I think that I should approach the Pro-Nuncio on Roger's behalf for some spiritual guidance, as he faces a great dilemma. If he accepts the archbishop's view and, by his inaction, supports the continued escalation of the arms race, then he risks incineration in this world. However, should he stand by his resolution of unilateralism, then he risks incineration in the next. It must be very worrying for him.

Wednesday, 1 June

A letter from the Greater London Council in response to my twinning suggestions. I must admit that I suspect the writer, Mr Simon Turney, to be not entirely serious in his reply. However, it certainly cheers up what is another black day (Roger deep in his sulks), and I am grateful to him for that. In return I will ask Letitia Odette if she has any home-made strawberry jam left. I'm sure Mr Turney would like a jar. What am I to do with Roger? I was so anxious for him to snap out of it that I even thought of inviting Mr Oliver around with his projector and slides of 'My Holiday in Yugoslavia'.

It never rains but it pours. The Morris Minor now has gearbox trouble and sounds like a cat being tortured when moving up from first. Maybe Roger will cheer up when we get our Challenger and take that for a spin along the country lanes. On the question of the purchase money for the Challenger, the Royal Ordnance Factory suggested applying for a bank overdraft. Not having an account, it is probably better to start negotiations at the top. Consequently some days ago

From: **Simon Turney**
Member of the Greater London Council
for Islington Central
Chairman, Public Services and
Fire Brigade Committee

MEMBERS' LOBBY
THE COUNTY HALL
LONDON SE1 7PB

26 May 1983

W. Morgan Petty, Esq.
3 Cherry Drive
Canterbury
Kent

Dear Mr Petty (and Roger)

I was delighted to read of your progress in declaring 3 Cherry Drive a Nuclear
Free Zone. Now that abolition hangs over the GLC, I wonder if we could move the
rump of London's NFZ into part of your garden if Mrs Thatcher wins the election.
We will bring our own bunkers (4 of them, but one has smelly drains and is "off
the run" - a very handy Pentagon phrase - until they are mended). Perhaps you
could have a word with Nos 1 and 5 to find out their views on nuclear free but
sewage-ridden drains. I suppose we ought to bring a few shop-soiled but barely
used War Planners. They will come in handy for the first harvest after the
holocaust.

Now about the tank and the F1-11: I am astounded at your moderation and lack of
ambition. You've forgotten the fire-engine and the Luftwaffe ought to be able to
arrange for a squadron of Starfighters to drop in.

I'm not surprised Michael Heseltine hasn't replied to you: we used to get answers
when he was at the Department of the Environment but the Ministry of Defence and
all those peppery admirals have obviously gone to his head. Pity, he was quite
promising in his mace-waving days.

On Manchester and the Hallé Orchestra, you've got it totally wrong. Music is the
second greatest threat to world peace. I'm keeping the LSO, the Amadeus String
Quartet and a bunch of able-bodied, guitar-picking punks called Wargasm up my
sleeve till the real negotiations start. Don't let on, will you. The real zero
option is no symphony orchestra West of the Urals or East of Lands End, a mutual
and balanced reduction in male voice choirs and moving Jimmy Young to the BBC's
World Service.

Yours sincerely

Simon Turney

I approached Lord Boardman, the Chairman of the National Westminster Bank. I have explained the position here and that our immediate problem is one of finance. I do not anticipate needing the whole of the £1.5 million as a loan if we receive enough items for the White Elephant Stall; if the weather is kind to us, this should raise four hundred pounds, leaving us with what I think is called, in bankers' parlance, 'a considerable shortfall'. I have therefore asked Lord Boardman whether the National Westminster Bank would be able to meet this shortfall, some one million, four hundred and ninety-nine thousand, six hundred pounds, in the form of an unsecured loan. When I discussed this matter with Roger he was very sceptical of the bank's willingness to lend so much without security but, as I pointed out to him, many banks, including I understand the Nat West, have made loans of a much shakier nature to countries like Brazil, Mexico and Poland.

Friday, 3 June

Recently Roger has suggested that we 'catch the programmes on the new tube', by which he means watch Channel Four. He says this is a must for *Guardian* readers. As the only time we get to watch any television is at the end of gardening/ manoeuvres and before sentry duty, it is usually late evening. I must say Channel Four is certainly different. Interviewers in shirts the colours of which would make even Mr Oliver faint, in uncomfortable-looking chairs and surrounded by empty polystyrene cups and cigarette ends. Added to which all the programmes look as though they have been made in the same Nissen hut. According to Roger, this gives the channel 'street credibility'. With all this increased air time to fill I was wondering whether Mr Isaacs, the Controller of Channel Four, would be interested in a little idea I have. Despite the reply we received from the Ministry of Agriculture about fall-out, I must admit to being a little worried about the post-nuclear position of the garden. According to Mr Bridger, insects are going to survive a nuclear attack almost intact. If

69

this is the case, then, with all the gardens around being destroyed, our vegetable patch will become extremely inviting to many times the normal number of pests. I did write to the Agricultural Research Council for advice in this matter some time ago, but unfortunately their reply seems to have gone astray in the post. What I have suggested to Mr Isaacs is that Channel Four might like to commission a series on 'Gardening after the Bomb' (I have told him to feel free to use my title if he wishes). It may be that, as only those people in nuclear free areas will be around to harvest their crop after a nuclear exchange, the programme will have a minority audience; but, as Roger points out, that was precisely what Channel Four was set up to cater for. On the question of a presenter, Roger would like to have a go. He is quite photogenic, and although he has no television experience he is very keen to learn. He would even, if it were absolutely necessary, wear one of those awful coloured shirts. On the subject of television, now that the general election is in full swing, thank heavens we shall be away on manoeuvres when it actually takes place and the small screen is full of party political broadcasts. It's a shame that Mrs Thatcher has such a bad cold, it makes her voice very husky and at times almost inaudible. I write to tell her how much Roger and myself missed her sharp, strident and, dare I say it, resolute tone. Roger's grandmother used to swear by cloves in lemon juice and I suggest she give that a try. If she does I am sure it won't be long before her voice is back to normal. I also take the opportunity to gently rebuke her for the failure to give us a few days' notice of the election announcement so that we could place a wager. Still, I suppose it was all a bit of a rush, her wanting to tell the nation before the *Daily Mail* did. No doubt she will in compensation send us a little something for our White Elephant Stall.

Saturday, 4 June

A letter from the United States. At first I thought, from its bulk, that it was our six hundred pounds. We could use it.

UNITED STATES ARMS CONTROL AND DISARMAMENT AGENCY

May 31, 1983

Mr. W. Morgan Petty
3 Cherry Drive
Canterbury, England

Dear Mr. Petty:

Your May 6, 1983 letter to Ambassador Adelman has
been referred to me for reply.

I am enclosing a speech by President Reagan, which
you may find interesting.

Thank you for writing and for your offer of help.

Sincerely,

Joseph D. Lehman

Enclosure:

March 31, 1983 Speech

from SIR MICHAEL TIPPETT

Publisher: Schott & Co. Ltd. 48 Great Marlborough Street, London, W1V 2BN Tel. (01) 437-1246/7/8
B. Schott's Söhne   Weihergarten 5   6500 Mainz   Germany.   Tel. 010 49 6131 24341
Agents: Ingpen & Williams.   14 Kensington Court, London W8 5DN.   Tel. (01) 937-5158
Herbert Barrett Management.   1860 Broadway, New York, N.Y. 10023   Tel. 010 1 212 245 3530

                                        c/o 48,Great Marlborough Street,
                                           London W1V 2BN

                                        2nd June 1983

W.Morgan Petty,Esq.,
3,Cherry Drive,
CANTERBURY,
Kent.

Dear Mr.Morgan Petty,

Sir Michael has asked me to write in reply to your letter of April 23rd,
and I am sorry that I was not in touch before.

He is very interested to learn that 3,Cherry Drive is now a nuclear-free
zone and glad that you have been prudent enough to retain strong conventional
forces. But are you sure that a First World War bayonet and a Swedish Cavalry
Officer's sword are quite sufficient ? The enemy hordes will doubtless be
equipped with devastating weaponry.

He is sorry that his schedule of composition is too busy at the moment to
consider writing something for you and Roger,although he does,of course,
recognize the importance of keeping the spirits high. It is a pity that
you and Roger are not sopranos,as you then might have sung Sir Michael's
arrangement of Blow's Ah Heaven ! What is't I hear ? As it is,you could
do worse than Men of Harlech - it worked very well in the film.

With all good wishes,

Yours sincerely,

Nicholas Wright

Instead it is from a Joseph D. Lehman replying for Ambassador Adelman in Geneva. He thanks us for our offer of help, from which I assume that they do not want Roger to go to Switzerland. He will be so disappointed. Enclosed with Mr Lehman's letter is a copy of what I think is now known as President Reagan's 'Star Wars' speech. On reading the full text, both Roger and myself are disappointed that there is no mention of converting microwave ovens. Also in the post is a note from Sir Michael Tippett. It seems he is too busy to consider writing a battle song especially for us and suggests we try, like Ivor Emmanuel in the film, 'Men of Harlech'. I have therefore planned a rehearsal for tomorrow evening and have asked Viola Odette, providing her legs are not playing her up too much, to accompany us on the piano. If the rehearsal goes well, I shall consider this as being our offering for the purpose of cultural exchanges. On that front, I have suggested to Mr Popov, the Soviet Ambassador, that we could perhaps arrange such an exchange with the U.S.S.R. I wonder if the Bolshoi Ballet are very busy in the autumn? I know how much Roger would enjoy seeing them. He had to give up his own ambitions in that direction because he grew too tall. If this could be arranged after the vegetable harvest it would be possible to put a platform at the bottom of the garden (once we had camouflaged all the classified equipment) where they could perform. I do not think our reciprocation to the Soviets should be martial in tone, and therefore I will substitute for 'Men of Harlech' Roger playing 'The Bluebells of Scotland' on the spoons, as I'm sure this would go down very well in Leningrad.

Sunday, 5 June

We leave on Wednesday for Operation Hollyhock. Eight weeks somewhere in the South of England, and there is such a lot to do in the garden before we go. Roger has bought one of those little white golf ball things that feed the fish so much a day while you're away. I think it is guilt, as one of the Koi carp is looking a little worse for wear since he exploded his

Chairman

National Westminster Bank PLC
41 Lothbury, London
EC2P 2BP

23rd May, 1983

Dear Mr Logan Petty

     Thank you for your letter of 14th May,
received today, in connection with your request for
a loan to purchase a new Challenger tank.

     Your plans appear most interesting, but I am
afraid the figures do not add up to what could be
termed "a viable banking proposition".

     May I suggest that if Roger and you work hard,
are lucky with the weather and your Bring and Buy
Sale raises £1,499,600, then you approach us again
with a revised request for the more manageable
shortfall of £400.

Yours Sincerely

Lord Boardman

W. Morgan Petty, Esq.,
3 Cherry Drive,
Canterbury,
Kent.

baked-bean-tin bomb near the edge of the pond. I thought it was dead until Roger brought it round with a bucket of salt water. It still does not look well. Our first casualty. Roger says if the carp does die it will have to be buried with full military honours, which I think is a little excessive for a fish.

Monday, 6 June

Roger has taken to blowing reveille in the morning. I must confess that his trumpet-playing is not very good and Mr Bridger, hearing it for the first time, thought it was an alarm and rang the fire brigade. When they arrived it was all very embarrassing, firemen running everywhere with their buckets and hoses, and their chief officer taking out his axe and preparing to knock down the front door. When I explained the mix-up and said even if there had been a fire, we had our own bucket of sand and hosepipe for dealing with it, the chief officer gave me a funny look and said something under his breath. The second post brings two letters. The first is from Lord Boardman at the National Westminster Bank. Unfortunately, he cannot loan us the full one and a half million pounds because he says it does not add up to a 'viable banking proposition'. However, he does say that if we raise the first £1,499,600 then the Nat West will see if it can manage the last four hundred. It's a start, I suppose. The second letter is from Marconi Space and Defence. I wrote to their Chairman some time ago outlining the position here and explaining that when we have built the Squirrel, and it becomes operational, then we will have to have an alert system. I know that Roger harbours secret ambitions to sit in a deck-chair, silk scarf around his neck, reading the *Guardian*, just as they did during the Battle of Britain. But this will be impractical, he has the garden to do. For the same reason he cannot sit in the cockpit all day waiting for an enemy attack. The answer would seem to be radar. My inquiry to Marconi was for something that would warn us long enough for Roger to sprint from the greenhouse and take off in time to confront the enemy. It

Marconi
Space & Defence Systems

Marconi Space & Defence Systems Limited
The Grove, Warren Lane
Stanmore, Middlesex HA7 4LY, England
Telephone: 01-954 1842 Telex: 22616

The Chairman

your ref:

our ref: HCT/JH

2nd June 1983

W Morgan Petty Esq.,
3 Cherry Drive,
CANTERBURY,
Kent

Dear Mr Morgan Petty,

        Thank you for your letter of 23rd May. Your
determination to defend your territory is an inspiration to
us all though there will be those who feel, as I do, that
you are not following the wiser elements in our country by
declaring your garden a nuclear-free zone. Obscurantism in
this respect is a strange accompaniment to the efficiency
and forethought which have clearly gone into your general
defensive plan. But let us not argue about that! You
need a radar and you do right to come to the Marconi
Company. We have the best and they all originate with our
Mr Chittenden, to whom I am sending your letter together
with a copy of this one.

        I do not, of course, know what provision has been
made in your Defence Budget for equipment of this kind. The
jump from Roger's garden fork to a 1983 model radar is not
inconsiderable, even when made via a squirrel. But no doubt
you have your own plans for increased taxation and/or recourse
to The City institutions.

        Whatever befalls I feel sure that we can rely on the
impregnability of 3 Cherry Drive.

                        Yours sincerely,

                        General Sir Harry Tuzo

Registered at London No. 964491   Registered Office: The Grove Warren Lane Stanmore Middlesex HA7 4LY
A management company for The Marconi Company Limited: A GEC-Marconi Electronics company Holding company: The General Electric Company p.l.c.

would also be helpful if it could give us notice of the impending arrival of starlings and wood pigeons which, despite the netting, are making a terrible mess of the early peas. The reply, signed by General Sir Harry Tuzo, tells us that we have come to the right place. The only problem now will be in paying for it.

Wednesday, 8 June

Reveille at 5.00 a.m. this morning. Whilst I admire Roger's dedication to duty, it certainly is interfering with my sleep. Today is his birthday. I have bought him a pair of army surplus gloves. As well as being a present, it will avoid my having to spend Defence Fund money on something similar for the autumn. He has had four cards, one from the Odette sisters, one from Mr Bridger, one of course from myself, and the last with a New Zealand stamp from his brother Malcolm who emigrated after he left school and who is now a hairdresser in Wellington. In the military post, there is a letter from Charles Saatchi. Unfortunately he feels that, as his company are already involved in political advertising, there would be a conflict of interest. There is also a letter from Channel Four. The colour of their notepaper is almost as bright as their presenters' shirts. I must admit, having read it, I'm not sure what it says, but I think the answer is negative. On a more positive note, the Electoral Reform Society are happy to undertake the counting of our referendum and on an expenses only basis. That's very good news. Still, as there is a big gap between most kinds of election, it probably leaves them with time to kill, and I suppose it's good for them to keep their hand in. This evening there was a small party for Roger. Viola Odette brought some oak-leaf wine, which I thought tasted like stewed moss, but which everybody else seemed to like. So much so in Mr Bridger's case that after his fifth glass he started talking to the barometer about the relative merits of fungicides. It was such a pity that when Roger went to blow out the candle on the cake, he closed his eyes to make a wish,

SAATCHI & SAATCHI COMPANY PLC.

REGISTERED OFFICE: 80 CHARLOTTE STREET, LONDON W1A 1AQ. TEL: 01-636 5060. TELEX: 261580.

June 6th, 1983

W. Morgan Petty Esq.,
3 Cherry Drive,
Canterbury,
Kent

Dear Mr. Morgan Petty,

Thank you for your letter.

It would of course be a great pleasure to have your advertising account, but I regret that we are already involved in political advertising and therefore could not act for you as this would present a conflict of interest.

It was most kind of you to think of us, and would you pass our thanks to Roger for his recommendation.

Kindest regards,

Charles Saatchi

5th June 1983

W Morgan Petty
3 Cherry Drive
Canterbury
KENT

Dear Mr Morgan Petty,

I am responding at his request to your letter to Jeremy Isaacs,
as your programme suggestion comes under my area of programming.

I have to say that our plans for gardening programmes are
laid in advance for the next year or more. Gardeners' Calendar
is transmitted on the first Thursday of every month in the
early evening. It should however interest you and Roger even
if the series are of wider applicability than nuclear gardening.
For myself, even the designation by Ken Livingstone of the
GLC area where I live as a nuclear free zone gives me no confidence that a nuclear blast would be as selective in its effect
as you appear to indicate. But that is not a relevant topic
for me to comment on.

I hope we all survive!

Yours sincerely,

Naomi E Sargant

Naomi E Sargant
SENIOR COMMISSIONING EDITOR
EDUCATION

THE
ELECTORAL REFORM
SOCIETY

6 Chancel Street, Blackfriars, London SE1 0UX.

President: The Hon. Dr. Garret FitzGerald, T.D.

From the Chief Executive: Seamus Burke (Direct Line: 01-928 1622)

4 June 1983

W. Morgan Petty, Esq.,
3, Cherry Drive,
Canterbury,
Kent.

Dear Mr. Morgan Petty,

Thank you for your letter of 19 May which was awaiting
my return from New York.

It was good of you to inform us of your decision and
to invite our assistance. Happily, we have a member
of our staff living in Kent and, in view of the
historic importance of your election, I am sure that
he would be prepared to undertake the duty on an
expenses only basis.

Yours sincerely,

SEAMUS BURKE

Enc.

and accidentally set alight his paper hat. Letitia Odette, thinking very quickly, poured a jug of blackcurrant cordial over him. It doused the fire but did leave him in quite a mess. Nobody noticed that Mr Bridger had disappeared until we heard the fire engines outside. It seems he saw the flames and, in his confused state, dialled 999. It was the same chief fire officer as before, and I think he took it very well, but he did not accept Viola Odette's offer of a glass of oak-leaf wine.

11.30 p.m. The revelries have ended. Tomorrow, 9 June 1983, is a momentous day. We, the defenders of Cherry Drive, leave for eight weeks of manoeuvres, 'somewhere in the South of England'. Roger has packed the tent, Camping Gaz and the hot water bottles. Under the cover of darkness, with the utmost secrecy and not forgetting to leave a note out for the milkman, we set out to test ourselves in a cold, hostile environment. I hope we are up to it. As I write this, Roger is out in the garden checking the defences for the final time before we leave. A little while ago, I heard a splash and a scream. All I hope is that he can get his uniform dry for the morning.

The intervening pages of *The Defence Diaries of W. Morgan Petty*, relating to the Operation Hollyhock summer exercises, have been removed for reasons of security, lest they provide valuable information to the enemy.

Thursday, 11 August

Back a week and so much to do. The weather while we were away has, according to Viola Odette, been glorious. Certainly the garden has run riot. When Roger returned he confessed to amazement at the size of his Scarlet Perfections. Mr Bridger agreed to put the hose over the vegetables each evening. Unfortunately, on one occasion he left the tap on, and now the slit trench is two foot deep in water. All I can hope is that, if we are to be attacked, it will have dried out beforehand. Spending long hours there during the course of a battle will do neither of us any good. Especially Roger, who has been complaining of twinges of rheumatism.

Saturday, 13 August

A day of reflection as I write up my official report on our manoeuvres. I must confess that they turned out to be a little trickier than I had at first thought. From those advertisements you see on television, I imagined them to be a mixture between scouting and a nature ramble, with the odd bang to keep you on your toes and farmers' wives rushing out with bowls of new laid eggs. Ours were not at all like that. I burned my hand rather badly on the Camping Gaz doing the bacon for breakfast, and later that day Roger dropped the Ordnance Survey map into the latrine. I wonder who thinks these television advertisements up? Roger says it was probably an 'ideas man' in an agency. Apparently one of these has recently joined the Camera Club. He is called Ralph and wears stripy shirts with stiff white collars. According to Roger he is considered very good at his job, on one occasion persuading thousands of people that cheese imported from Nanking, in the People's Republic of China, was indistinguishable from Double Gloucester, and the success of that campaign won him an award.

Ralph and Roger share a mutual interest in portraiture, and one evening while they were waiting for the model to turn up he says Ralph 'put it on the line'. It seems the secret of advertising is not knowing anything about the 'product', as in that way the truth can't inhibit your creativity. As Ralph's nearest link with things military would seem to be watching the Trooping of the Colour on television, he might be the person who dreamt up the farmer's wife and eggs scenario. Roger has promised to ask him next time they meet. I express my surprise that a man like Mr Heseltine, who has himself done military service, however short, and who must ultimately be held responsible for the dissemination of information about the armed services, should allow such an unrealistic picture to be shown.

Tuesday, 16 August

This morning while Roger is hacking away at the dandelions I have a chance to go through the military post that arrived in our absence. The first is a letter from Mr MacGregor at British Steel. Unfortunately, they say they cannot help us with our request for material for the Squirrel. This is extremely odd, as only last evening there was talk on the wireless about the huge over-capacity of the Corporation. If this is the attitude they adopt to potential purchasers it is no wonder Roger says they are losing one million pounds a day. They suggest that I try the smaller steel outlets. Before I do, I shall have a word with Mr Bridger, as he may have some more rusted-out buckets, or know of someone who does. The second letter is from the Manpower Services Commission. They say they are 'keen to support training schemes for young people involving familiarization with and the use of new technology' and they ask that we contact them again when our ideas for building the Squirrel are further developed. This will please Roger enormously. I know he is well advanced on the initial design as I have seen it chalked up on the inside of the shed door. The last missive is a photocopied note from the Apostolic Pro-Nuncio. Apparently he has gone abroad. I must say I find this a bit off, stirring up all this trouble, upsetting Roger, and then going on holiday.

I.M.P. EVANS
SECRETARY OF THE CORPORATION
AND DIRECTOR, LEGAL SERVICES

BRITISH STEEL CORPORATION

9 ALBERT EMBANKMENT
LONDON SE1 7SN

01-735 7654
TELEX NO. 916061
7th June, 1983.

IMPE/SFC

W. Morgan Petty, Esq
3, Cherry Drive,
Canterbury,
Kent.

Dear Mr. Petty,

       I have been asked to reply to your letter of the 17th May, the contents of which have been noted.

       I'm afraid it is not possible for the Corporation to help you in the way you propose, but I would suggest that you consider getting in touch with one of the many outlets where steel is sold in small quantities to meet specific needs.

       Yours sincerely,

ImpEvans

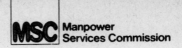

Selkirk House
166 High Holborn
London
WC1V 6PF

Telephone: 01-836 6126

Chairman: David Young

W. Morgan Petty, Esq.,
3 Cherry Drive,
Canterbury,
Kent.

Dear Mr. Petty

     Thank you for your letter of 20th May addressed to
David Young.

     I am sorry that you have been unable to fill your two
vacancies for gardening guerillas. I was interested to read
of your efforts to obtain air defence for 3 Cherry Drive and
am most impressed by your plans.

     It is pleasing to note that the publicity associated
with the light aircraft built by Youth Opportunities Programme
trainees in Sunderland made an impression on you. The Commission
was most encouraged by the success of that project and has receive
proposals for other similar projects. Yours, however, is one
of the most sophisticated.

     The Commission is keen to support training schemes
for young people involving familiarisation with and the use
of new technology and the project you suggest would undoubtedly
offer such opportunities. Unfortunately, what you are actually
proposing is not clear from your letter and at this stage I
am uncertain if your project would be suitable for Commission
support. If and when your ideas are further developed, you
might like to contact us again.

yours sincerely

David Vere

David Vere
Private Secretary

APOSTOLIC NUNCIATURE

54 PARKSIDE
LONDON, SW19 5NF

TELEPHONE: 01-946 1410

In the absence of the Apostolic Pro-Nuncio,
Archbishop Bruno B. Heim, the Apostolic Nunciature
is happy to acknowledge receipt of the letter which
you recently addressed to the Pro-Nuncio.

While thanking you, the Apostolic Nunciature
assures you that the contents of your letter will
be brought to the attention of the Pro-Nuncio
on his return to this country.

Date as postmark.

Roger has a new friend called Ingrid. She popped around while he was digging potatoes. They met, so he tells me, when he took our camouflage netting, which was getting very grubby, to the launderette to use their tumble dryer. She seems a nice enough young lady although I was a bit put off at first by the jumper she was wearing. Bright purple with an orange parrot in the middle. Over coffee she tells me she is a 'feminist poet', and she has lent Roger a book. It is called *Female Politics and their Place in Horticulture*. At first I thought it was a joke, but when I started to chuckle, one glance made me quite sure it wasn't. She has made Roger promise to read it by next Monday, when she says she will come again. It is rather a thick book, with very close print, and I tried, tactfully, to point out that, as Roger was already very busy with urgent defence work, he might not be able to get the whole way through and wasn't there a shorter version instead. Unfortunately Ingrid became a little agitated and insisted that he must, as she said nothing was as important as the onward march of the women's movement. In the afternoon Mr Oliver appears. He has two tickets for an exhibition of new Japanese enlargers. He was intending to go with Michael Hardiman, but they have had a tiff over something or other, and he was wondering whether Roger would like to go instead. Roger looked at the tickets and then said very casually that he couldn't as it was next Monday and he'd already made arrangements to see another friend then. Mr Oliver left, a little flushed. Oh dear, I just hope all this doesn't end in tears.

Saturday, 27 August

Today, Roger spent the morning busy on the new observation platform he is building in the Beauty of Bath apple tree. From the top he can see quite a long way, or will be able to when he has clipped a bit off the privet. This new development is part of a re-appraisal of our overall strategy. Our new plan is for me to hold the enemy down between the greenhouse and the chrysanthemums at what we understand in military terms is called a 'choke point'. I do not anticipate a lunge by enemy forces across the lawn at the back, as this is clearly signed 'KEEP OFF THE GRASS'. Then at the right moment Roger, in the Squirrel, will attempt to cut off the enemy's forward positions by a series of low-level sweeps across the shiplap fencing. There is one small flaw in this strategy, and that is that Roger is also supposed to be directing operations from the observation tower, and it would be unreasonable to expect him to be in two places at once. I shall have to work on this. It is important, so he tells me, that we cover the top of the observation platform. Unfortunately, inquiries amongst local drapers reveal that those that do stock camouflage material have it marked up at three pounds a yard. I therefore send Roger off to a jumble sale, advertised on a lamp-post by the Whitstable road, with the two pounds and sixteen pence that remain in our Defence Fund. He has instructions to purchase whatever odds and ends of material he thinks will enable us to make our own. (I shall ask Letitia Odette, who is very handy with a needle, to run this up for us.) Roger returns triumphant; he has found two summer frocks which should dye nicely and a string bag which we can pull down for guy ropes. He has also spent ten pence on a record from a language course called 'Speak Russian in Seven Days'. It is a little scratched but, despite the hiss, usable. Unfortunately, it does not contain much in the way of military vocabulary – I think this was probably on another record in the set – but nevertheless it has a great number of useful everyday phrases: 'My library book is overdue', and 'Just a quick trim at the sides, I'm in a hurry'. I suppose it would be too much to hope that, should we be attacked, the advance guard will be made up of conscripted librarians and hairdressers.

Thursday, 1 September

Yesterday Ingrid came to tea and today Roger is now engrossed in a book called *Women – Did They Discover America First?*, which she says is a thesis proving that a shipful of female Vikings landed there long before Christopher Columbus. Ingrid is a nice girl if a little intense. After tea (Roger made scones especially) we were treated to the première of her new work. It is a paean to female bricklayers in Murmansk. I am afraid that it is not to my taste, having constant reference to sexual harassment behind concrete-mixers and the failure of the male bricklayers to fulfil their quota. It seems the idea of this new poetry is for the writer to read a verse and then for everybody to discuss it. Frankly, after verse one, I couldn't think of anything to say, but Roger, to break an embarrassing silence, did ask if she knew what colour bricks in Murmansk were? I think I rather put my foot in it by inquiring if she liked Wordsworth, being told very firmly that he was a 'chauvinist lackey in the pay of the state and a conspirator in female oppression'. I must say I hadn't thought of him in quite that way before. After verse thirty, I managed to excuse myself on the grounds of urgent defence business. However, Roger had to sit through it all and, three hours later, barely had time to change out of his gardening clothes for sentry duty, leaving, I must add, a long list of military tasks undone. Female emancipation or not, I shall have to put my foot down.

Saturday, 3 September

At last the day arrives for the 'Challenger for Cherry Drive' Bring and Buy. I must admit all was not quite as I had planned it. By eleven o'clock only Roger, Mr Bridger and the Odette sisters were there to hear my speech. It seems that Roger, still slightly under the weather, forgot to telephone the Automobile Association to ask them to put up signs showing the exact location, and the large red and white poster that we put on the corner last night seems to have been stolen. I delayed getting to my feet with my words of welcome as long as possible, hoping for a horde of late arrivals. However, I could see that Letitia, who cannot stand for very long, was becoming agitated. What is more, a number of dark clouds were heading in our direction. I had in fact just managed to finish my speech when the rain began. It is indeed an ill wind that blows no good as, having so little to sell and so few to buy, we held our sale in the living room. The Odette sisters bought the spider plants that Roger had potted and we in turn bought both jars of their strawberry preserve, raising £1.10. Nobody seemed terribly interested in the S.D.P. White Paper on Defence and so I gave it to Mr Bridger who has just purchased some new wellington boots. These are a little on the large side and he has stuffed half this document into each toe. I am sure Dr Owen would be pleased to know that we had found it so useful.

Monday, 5 September

We had barely finished emptying the last few inches of water from the bottom of the slit trench (where we found three Red Bellied Newts which Roger says are quite rare and which he later released into the garden pond) when Mr Oliver arrived with Michael Hardiman. It seems they have made it up, and the purpose of their visit was to tell Roger that they won't be at the Camera Club for the next two weeks as they have booked an 'Autumn Break' holiday in Ibiza. Mr Oliver (ghastly yellow shirt) was in one of his superior moods and said that they would have asked Roger to join them but knew how busy he was with the defence work. Roger, who was at the time standing covered in mud and holding the plastic bucket he had used for bailing, pretended not to hear this remark. Mr Oliver, looking around, then asked where, if the Red Army were to surrender, we were going to keep the prisoners. I cannot be sure but I thought I detected a hint of sarcasm in his voice. However, sarcasm or not, this is something that I had not considered before. Fighting off an army is one thing, but taking them prisoner is quite another. Even a hundred or two burly Mongol soldiers would cause enormous problems. For a start, we only have two spare rooms. Then there is the question of changing the sheets and feeding them. Undoubtedly some will have special dietary requirements for religious or cultural reasons. The more I think about it, the more urgent the problem becomes. What we really need is some advice on how to secure peace, as victors, without turning the house and garden into a sort of Butlin's for prisoners awaiting repatriation. I shall write to Dr Henry Kissinger, the former United States Secretary of State, for advice on this one. I mentioned this intention to Roger, who said the last he heard Mr Kissinger was heavily involved with preparations for the World Cup. Surely not as a player? Even Sir Stanley Matthews had to retire at fifty.

Saturday, 10 September

There are some days when, despite the threat of invasion by hostile forces, I think I should have stayed in bed. Operation Clematis (so called because it involved a great deal of climbing) was a disaster. The object was to test our, or rather Roger's, prowess at crossing a mined area. Not having any actual mines, we denoted the danger zone with the lids of coffee jars, though to make it more realistic Roger did put up a sign with a skull and crossbones on it and I found a thunderflash left over from last year when we had the Odette sisters around for bonfire night. All was going quite well, with Roger spreadeagled across the rope bridge, pulling himself along by his hands. It was at this point that I threw the thunderflash. I had not told Roger of its existence, as I wanted to test his reaction to sudden explosions. I think this was a mistake as, with the bang, he jerked up and down on the rope bridge before one end gave way and he fell rather awkwardly on to the newly erected sign. Fortunately he is not badly injured, but when I took him a cup of tea and some aspirin he was rather sharp, saying 'somebody had not been practising their reef knots'. In this kind of mood I have found it is always better to leave him on his own. I wonder if that's the approach they adopt in the S.A.S.?

In the light of our experiences yesterday, I reflect again on the necessity for some formal military training. The reply to our request for details of a sandwich course at Sandhurst seems to have gone astray in the post, or maybe they are full up. Roger says we should try somewhere else. The French Military Academy is the nearest, but still far enough away for us to have to board. I must admit that I am not too keen on the École Militaire as, though Roger has an O-level in the language, I have barely a dozen words – a handicap which once led me, on a day trip to Boulogne, into ordering three uncooked cauliflowers and the waiter's left shoe for lunch. I think in the circumstances we had better stick to the mother tongue, which leaves us with the United States Military Academy at West Point. Together we compose a letter explaining our position and giving details of our recent manoeuvres. I do not dwell on the problems we encountered, except to say that had it not been for a fortunate meeting with a rambler and his wife, Roger and myself might still be lost amongst the foliage of the English countryside, our navigation having gone a little awry. Again we request details of a sandwich course, or what Roger translates into American as 'a segregated knowledge acquiring situation interspersed with practical application scenarios'. The Defence Fund being as low as it is I suggest that we might approach the Department of Education and Science for a student grant. Roger, who is still in a bit of a sulk (not helped by the arrival of a postcard from Mr Oliver showing sun-drenched beaches under the caption 'Wish you were here'), says this will be a complete waste of time as Sir Keith Joseph, the Secretary of State, was trying to reduce the educational system to private tutors for the rich and church schools for potential clergy. I think he gets these somewhat radical ideas from the *Guardian* newspaper. However, my own reading of the situation is rather different. Whatever other areas of education the government may have to starve of cash, I am sure that defence will remain untouched, even if it means children have to write on slates and sit on the floor in unheated classrooms. After all, they have made it quite clear that their aim is to protect our way of life.

Friday, 16 September

Battle stations at 5.00 a.m. Awakened by the baked-bean-tin alarm, I discover Roger already combing the undergrowth for the intruder. Finding nothing, he was about to return to his sentry duty and I to my bed when there was a sudden movement under the rhododendron. Without hesitation, Roger charged forward and lunged with the fork. I am still not quite sure how he managed to plunge the prongs through his foot, but it is nothing that a bathe in Dettol and a few days' rest will not put right. Just as I am helping him back to the house a large black and white cat appears from beneath the bush and slinks away into the night. Seeing it go, I notice Roger is near to tears.

Saturday, 17 September

I invite the Odette sisters to come for a sing-song. Unfortunately Viola's legs are playing her up again, which rules out the piano. Instead we hum along to a gramophone recording of 'The Blue Danube Waltz'. Roger sits in the corner, his bandaged foot raised up on a stool. He asks that I do not tell Ingrid (who arrives later with some home-made muesli yogurt as a get-well gift) the details of how he received his injury, as after all our training he feels somewhat foolish being injured in combat by a cat. Ingrid spends some time without success trying to persuade Letitia Odette to join her Women's Group and announces that she will read us her new poem, 'The Amazons of N.W.3', which is a tribute to feminist squatters in Hampstead who have set up a non-sexist art centre in a derelict wine bar. Unfortunately she seems to have left it at home. We must be thankful for small mercies.

Monday, *19 September*

Our little soirée the other evening has given me an idea for fund-raising (heaven knows, with just over one pound in the Defence Fund, we need it). We shall hold a musical evening. On the question of performers, naturally my first choice would be Viola Odette, but given her legs I fear I shall have to look elsewhere. Roger suggests somebody called André Previn, who is an American. I am a little put off by the fact that he is an erstwhile jazz musician. That sort of music always conjures up in my mind pictures of sweaty men picking their teeth in cellars full of ladies of ill repute. However, Roger tells me that Mr Previn is very respectable and spends most of his time in evening dress on an orchestra podium. Having marked out on the floor of the lounge the area that would be covered by a grand piano, I think we will have room for about ten persons. I know it is not quite the Albert Hall, but what we lack in numbers I am sure we shall make up for in appreciation. I suggest to Mr Previn that the programme consist mainly of Beethoven, with perhaps the odd Slavonic Dance thrown in if we are honoured by Mr Andropov's presence. I have also asked for some indication of his fees.

Wednesday, *21 September*

A fine autumn day, and what is more we have finished the observation tower. With the help of a bottle of elderflower wine, Roger, Mr Bridger and myself have what is I believe called in builders' parlance a 'topping out ceremony'. I must say I am very impressed with the dyed frocks from the jumble sale. They make the post very difficult to see even from a short distance, and Roger putting lace around the edges was a nice touch. The next stage in the construction plan is the Command Bunker. It is becoming increasingly tedious having to take down all the maps in the dining and living rooms when people pop in. I do not intend that it should be a very elaborate affair, just a lounge, bedroom and conveniences (with perhaps a garage for the Challenger) and a view out over the rose bushes, the most likely direction of attack. As with the observation tower, I shall do the administration whilst Roger sets about the construction. I think it would be a good idea though, given his other commitments, to share part of the work, and to that end I ask if he can think of a good painter. He mentions David Hockney. I have therefore written for an estimate. I tell Mr Hockney that we will want two coats of emulsion in a soothing colour (prolonged military engagement might necessitate our staying inside for some considerable time) and matching gloss on the window frames. Since posting the letter I have learned that, despite his Bond Street address, Mr Hockney lives in California, quite a long way away. Still, I suppose he will have a van.

Friday, 23 September

I have dropped Lord Boardman, at the National Westminster, a line explaining our plans for a musical evening and our invitation to Mr Previn. Perhaps he would like to come too. Both Roger and myself were very touched by his kind offer to help with the purchase of the Challenger and, as one good turn deserves another, I have asked whether, at times of high international tension, his bank would like to keep its money in our garden shed. Then, after the thermonuclear conflagration, they can send someone round to collect it. I am sure that the Nat West's customers would be only too delighted if, having to put up with the inconvenience of a nuclear war, they knew that their money was safe. I tell him that the shed is eight foot by six and that there are no security problems, Roger having fitted a large key-operated lock. (We used to have combination locks but Roger kept forgetting the numbers and it became very expensive sawing them off to get at the garden tools.) If by some chance they have more money than will fit into the shed, then I am sure that the attic will take the overflow. It might be that after a nuclear exchange many of their branches will be destroyed and that they would like to open a sub-office here. Just in case, I remind Roger to get some spare batteries for the calculator I gave him last Christmas. I'm sure Lord Boardman will reimburse us.

Sunday, 25 September

Ingrid has, she tells us over lunch, written a play. Encouraged by her friends at WAVE (Roger seems to think this means Women Against Virtually Everything), who she hopes will perform the work, it is, she says, a searing attack on male values. Roger, who is still in the doghouse having not finished the Viking Saga on time, offers to read this straight away but is told it is not a work for men and, as with all great art, you need to be a woman to understand the significance (something which Ingrid says is cosmic). I could not tell whether his sigh was one of rejection or relief. Whilst she is rewriting Act Two about female oppression and Roger and I are doing the washing up, I suggest that we do our own bit helping the theatre by offering a home to some of the more valuable theatre relics that might otherwise be destroyed in a nuclear war. There is some room in the spare wardrobe. Roger thought this a very good idea and said that his great theatrical idol Donald Sinden, who he still remembers as being 'magical' in *London Assurance* at the Aldwych many years ago, is by coincidence something of a prime mover in the attempt to establish a theatre museum. We may not be able to preserve the palace of Hampton Court for future generations but we may be able to save Gertrude Lawrence's knickers from being reduced to ashes. I shall write to Mr Sinden straight away.

Thursday, 29 September

A letter arrives from I. J. Smith, personal assistant to Lord Boardman. It appears that his lordship is in Washington at a meeting of the International Monetary Fund. I must confess that neither Roger nor myself has any idea what the International Monetary Fund is. Roger belonged to an Inter-

DONALD SINDEN, C.B.E., F.R.S.A.

28 September 1983

W Morgan Petty
3 Cherry Drive
Canterbury
Kent

Dear W Morgan Petty,

Many thanks for your letter of 22 September.

Donald Sinden has asked me to say how very kind of
you it is to offer shelter to theatrical memoribilia,
but the V & A have them all in safe storage until
the theatre museum opens in 1985.

Thank you again for taking the trouble to write.

Yours sincerely,

Ms Leaflyn Jones
Secretary to Donald Sinden

Chairman

National Westminster Bank PLC
41 Lothbury, London
EC2P 2BP

28th September 1983

Dear Mr Petty,

  Thank you for your letter of 21st September
addressed to Lord Boardman. I am acknowledging
receipt as the Chairman is in Washington at the
meeting of the International Monetary Fund.

  Whilst the content of your letter is undoubtedly
of major importance, I have decided against sending
a telex to Washington but I will ensure that your
letter is brought to the Chairman's attention, as
a priority matter, immediately upon his return.

Yours sincerely

I. J. Smith
Personal Assistant to
The Chairman

W. Morgan Petty Esq
3 Cherry Drive
Canterbury
Kent

national Stamp Club once, and perhaps it's a bit like that, where they sit around and, instead of showing off their rare stamps, show off instead the bundles of banknotes that they've collected. We have still not heard from Sir Keith Joseph about our student grants for West Point but, when the cheque arrives, and we make our arrangements to visit the United States, I shall add this International Monetary Fund to our list of places of interest and satisfy my curiosity.

Sunday, 2 October

Mr Oliver is moving to East Anglia. Apparently he and Michael Hardiman are buying a tea shop just outside Norwich. Roger took this sudden news surprisingly well. I think that secretly, when his thoughts are not taken up with preparations to survive a nuclear war and the increased resistance of garden pests to natural herbicides, his own dreams are of such a place, with window-boxes full of bright flowers, home-made shortbread and customerized doilies. I must admit though that I, for one, will not be sorry to see Mr Oliver go. After lunch we make an alarming discovery: the wheelbarrow we were planning to use to ferry ammunition during a battle, and in which Roger has been gathering the last of the leaves, has lost a handle, becoming difficult and dangerous to steer. This is the second piece of military equipment to become unserviceable in a week. (The clapper fell out of the alarm bell on Friday.) Such a setback causes me to write to Mrs Thatcher with an idea I have had for some time. I do not know if she is aware of the fact, but many large companies give discounts on the use of their products, services, etc., to shareholders, and knowing how keen she is on privatization I was wondering if it had occurred to her to sell off shares in the army. Then people like myself with an interest in defence could, for a modest investment, use their tanks, personnel carriers, howitzers, etc., at a cut rate. On manoeuvres Roger's feet became terribly blistered after a route march, something that could have been avoided had we the use of a Saracen armoured car. I also mention to Mrs Thatcher that her little something for the White Elephant Stall didn't arrive and suggest that she has a word with the post office at her end.

Friday, 7 October

Awoke to a loud banging and crackling and the garden covered by palls of dense black smoke. At first I feared the worst, that World War Three had started. As it turned out it was Mr Bridger burning garden rubbish on top of which he had placed damp sacking. Roger and I had a long meeting after this, as to be perfectly frank neither of us would recognize a thermonuclear explosion if we saw one, and it would be very embarrassing if we confused it with some other non-nuclear detonation. I suppose one way of assessing whether an explosion was nuclear would be by the amount of damage done. However there seems to be an awful lot of conflicting evidence about precisely what this would be. Sometimes when I listen to Mr Heseltine I get the impression that hiding away under the stairs with a thermos flask and a good book is an adequate precaution. However it has to be borne in mind that he has never actually seen a nuclear explosion and so couldn't really be expected to know what he was talking about. What we really need is an eye-witness account. Roger tells me James Cameron, a pensioner who writes for the *Guardian*, has seen nearly all of them since they started. Therefore if anyone were to know the difference between a conventional and a nuclear explosion it would be him. Maybe he has some old press cuttings? In which case, should Roger be out pruning the roses, and see an explosion over the fence, he can check with these and then, if it is nuclear, pop in and let me know straight away.

Friday, 14 October

Work progresses, if slowly, on the Command Bunker. Ingrid insists on helping with the digging despite the fact that the ground is heavy and wet. After a few minutes she looks exhausted and I suggest she make some tea instead. Roger takes me aside and explains confidentially that although Ingrid cannot do manual work, stopping her from trying would be 'sexist'. I am confused, as the logical result of this would be a waste of time and energy and, in Ingrid's case, possible injury. Roger agrees but, nodding sagely, says this is the price you pay for progress. I am still musing on what I am sure is a subtle philosophical point when a monoplane appears in the distance. Hurriedly Roger tries to cover up evidence of our work and we stand around looking nonchalant until the aircraft has passed. It is not until it is gone that we find Ingrid struggling out from beneath the tarpaulin. It appears that in his haste Roger did not notice that she was standing on the edge. I must admit I never thought I would hear such language from a woman. Roger went quite purple, and I was only thankful there was no one else around. All in all this is not an experience that I would wish to repeat, and I resolve to close my airspace to civilian traffic during the period of bunker construction. I do not foresee any difficulty as I understand from Roger that the Civil Aviation Authority were only too happy to oblige the United States Air Force when they had a similar problem, during building work, at somewhere called Greenham Common. I have therefore written to the Chairman telling him that this closure will come into effect as from 00.01 hours on Monday, 31 October. I ask him to inform the world's airlines of the position, and to assist him in this I enclose a plan showing the area to be avoided.

Thursday, 20 October

Mr Bridger has his picture in the local paper. At the Gardening Society show his Musselburgh leeks and Ulster Ensign potatoes won first prizes and his Dobie's Yardstick received a highly commended. I know for a fact that Roger had been keen to enter a marrow he was growing in the greenhouse. Unfortunately the last two bottles of Guinness he gave it rather overdid things, and, with a deafening bang, it exploded, breaking two panes of glass. I tried to cheer him up, in what has not been a good week, by quipping that with enough marrows we could hold off an enemy indefinitely, but he just glared and walked away. I am sure that if he could have a little publicity by way of acknowledgement for all his hard work he would feel better. It is quite by coincidence that in a copy of the London *Evening Standard* (a very popular newspaper amongst gardeners in this area, because for some strange reason it holds moisture better and is, therefore, used for lining seed boxes) I find an article about the Ministry of Defence allowing journalists to accompany them on battle exercises. Both Roger and myself feel strongly that the public should know the full horrors of warfare, the blood, the gore, the damp socks and the way that salt goes solid in plastic bags if you don't tie the top tightly enough. It may therefore be possible to kill two birds with one stone by inviting a journalist to accompany us on our next exercise planned for the spring of 1984. (Candidly I am glad we were not accompanied by the press on our summer manoeuvres as it would have been extremely bad for morale had a photograph of Roger dropping our Ordnance Survey map in the latrine been splashed across the world's front pages.) The question now is who to ask. Roger wanted to invite Max Hastings, but as he did not donate to our White Elephant Stall I don't see why we should. My own preference is for John Pilger who I believe is an Australian and for that reason will doubtless have a great deal of experience sitting around a glowing billycan in the outback, under the stars, and swapping stories, something that would while away the hours on night exercises. I shall extend an invitation straight away.

Friday, 28 October

Roger has built a scale model of the Squirrel using balsa wood and glue. I must say it is very impressive with its swept-back wings and little plastic canopy. Thoughtfully he has provided a window at the side where the pilot can lean out if he is feeling airsick. The Odette sisters complimented him on his inventiveness and Letitia, who has always been the more spirited of the two, has even asked to be taken up for a spin when it is completed. She tells us she has only flown once, to Oberammergau for the Passion play, on a British Airways scheduled flight, and is sure that a trip in a lethal killing machine like the Squirrel would be much more exciting. The bad news comes when Roger presents me with the budget. At £200,000 without the 'weapons fit', it is more expensive than I had anticipated, and we still only have eight pounds in the Defence Fund. We shall just have to work jolly hard to make the musical evening a great success. One idea I have had is to provide a buffet supper. I was going to ask Lady Olga Maitland to organize this, but she seems far too busy holding demonstrations in Trafalgar Square. What we really need is someone with an ingratiating manner but who can be firm with staff. Roger recommends Mrs Edwina Currie. I must confess her name is new to me, but apparently she has been recently elected an M.P. and has strong views on defence. He says she reminds him of Miss Lackett, a teacher at his primary school who had precisely these qualities. I have therefore written to Mrs Currie asking her to undertake the catering. Although I shall leave the final menu to her discretion I suggest something simple – cheese flan, jacket potatoes. Both Viola and Letitia have, despite their advanced years, offered to help with the serving. Luckily they still possess uniforms from their days as Nippies before the war.

Monday, 7 November

A letter arrives from the Civil Aviation Authority. I must say I find its tone rather snooty. It appears that in order to stop civil aircraft flying over our Nuclear Free Zone Roger and myself must obtain a statutory instrument. We are completely foxed by this, neither of us knowing what a statutory instrument is, and find no reference to it in the dictionary. Perhaps

DA/ATS
Room T1314
National Air Traffic Services
CAA House
45–59 Kingsway
(main entrance Kemble Street)
London WC2B 6TE
Telephone 01-379 7311   (Extn 2314)

NATS

Mr W Morgan Petty
3 Cherry Drive
Canterbury
<u>Kent</u>

Our Ref   8SB/317/29

Date   2 November 1984

Dear Mr Petty,

The Chairman of the Authority, Mr John Dent, has asked me to reply to
your letter to him of the 22 October 1983.

The power to prohibit aircraft from flying over any area in the UK is
exercisable only by an appropriate statutory instrument and the
Authority therefore cannot act unilaterally in this context.

However, I think you will agree that in practice the use of such powers
in respect of the premises which you occupy would be fraught with
difficulty, given the size and speed of modern transport aircraft.

I regret I cannot be more helpful.

Yours sincerely

P J RUTHERFORD
Director of Administration

A Joint Civil Aviation Authority — Ministry of Defence Service it's some kind of special siren. I shall make inquiries. The letter goes on to say that avoiding our zone will be fraught with difficulty given the size and speed of modern transport aircraft. Military necessity dictates an uncompromising attitude in this matter, and I urge Mr Rutherford at the Civil Aviation Authority to take a firm line with the world's airlines on our behalf. If they anticipate flying near to our Nuclear Free Zone then they can either use smaller and slower aircraft or be more careful. To help them even further I have asked Roger to string white ribbon up around our perimeter during the day and put a candle in a red painted jam jar in each corner at night.

Friday, 11 November

This afternoon a man with a small briefcase knocks at the door. At first I thought he was selling double glazing and so I hid behind the curtains. However it turns out that he is from the Church of the Twentieth Century Gospel. I admit that I have never heard of them, but he says this is not surprising as they are new to the area. From what I can make out they basically believe in the Holy Quartet: God the Father, God the Son, God the Holy Ghost and an American gentleman called Sam Jezelvitch. This is certainly a novel approach, and I ask what their church's position on nuclear weapons is? It seems Pastor Jezelvitch is all in favour, having stock in some of the larger corporations that manufacture them. I politely decline his offer to attend their inaugural service but he leaves some leaflets anyway. This business of the Church and the Bomb is very perplexing. I had rather believed the function of religion was to bring people together and promote peace, but now it seems that it can equally be used as a justification for annihilating them. A situation not helped by the meddling of politicians. Leading amongst these, according to Roger, is somebody called Gummer, who has just taken over as Chairman of the Conservative Party and bears an uncanny resemblance to an old friend of his who gave up his job with London

Transport and now runs a topless bar in Amsterdam. I know Roger is still greatly upset by the ambiguous attitude of the Church and so I shall drop Mr Gummer a line to ask his advice.

Sunday, 13 November

Mr Bridger stops by with some sweet william cuttings which he suggests we plant around the top of the slit trench to give it a homely touch. He asks if I am aware of the government's plan to alert the population to the arrival of a nuclear strike. It seems they suggest that when the strike is imminent, people aware of that fact should bang dustbin lids on the ground, blow whistles, shout, and generally make as much noise as possible to alert those who are not. I must say I can't see very much sense in this as everyone will undoubtedly know very soon. Given our nuclear free status such a course of action will not be necessary within the confines of our zone, but a similar exercise for alerting us to the approach of a Soviet division might be of use. Therefore, along with Roger, Mr Bridger and Viola Odette, who dropped around with a freshly made roly-poly, I tried this, Mr Bridger banging buckets with his spade, Roger shouting and shaking a tin of marbles, and Viola Odette swinging a football rattle. I must say we were making a very creditable din. It was just after our sixth rehearsal, when we were getting into the swing of it, that the police arrived. Apparently someone had complained. I told the constable why we were doing it and he seemed a little surprised, saying that this was the first they had ever heard of this plan. I suggested that he use his walkie-talkie and contact the station. Perhaps there has been some sort of bureaucratic bungle which should be sorted out immediately. It would be sad if people following government instructions to alert their neighbours should have their last few minutes on earth haunted by the prospect of arrest.

Thursday, 17 November

There is a great deal on the wireless today about the United States' recent invasion of Grenada, with senior Congressmen arguing that America should use its military power around the world to 'adjust' situations that it considers unfavourable. Our house and garden are politically non-aligned, something I made plain to Mr Reagan in a letter a while ago. However we are opposed to the siting of nuclear missiles on our territory, which Roger says may leave 'a gap on the Big Board at the Pentagon'. He further suggests that, given their present mood, the United States government might invade us and 'adjust' the situation here. I tell him that he is being unnecessarily alarmist and that we are sovereign territory and, technically I suppose, within the Commonwealth, but he points out, to my dismay, so was Grenada. I must say I do not relish coming home from the shops and finding G.I.s all over the place, barbecuing steaks and turning the back garden lawn into a baseball diamond. I am, on reflection, alarmed by the extraordinary number of recent visits we have had from clean-cut young men claiming to be window-cleaners, something which Roger says is a well-known cover story used by members of the Central Intelligence Agency. I have decided to take the bull by the horns and write a letter to Mrs Jeanne Kirkpatrick, the American ambassador to the United Nations, asking quite bluntly whether the United States has any plans to 'effect a rescue, pacification and regularization scenario' (invade us) here at 3 Cherry Drive. If not, I ask for a brief note confirming this; then if we find any 'doughboys' in our front garden we can point out their mistake and ask them to leave.

Monday, 21 November

Mr Bridger spent the weekend at his brother Arthur's and was telling him about our plans for a musical evening. The good news is that Arthur, a former quarter-finalist in the Pub Pianist of the Year Competition, has offered to loan us his instrument. Being upright in nature it will not be as pleasing to the eye as a grand piano, but it will save us the cost of hiring and leave room for more seats. Mr Bridger, who says the instrument is currently in his brother's shed, tells me that it is 'utility', which means, of course, that it was built during the war from available materials. How very appropriate, and I am sure that if we varnish the back and place it at an angle to the wall the words 'Ceylon Tea' will hardly be visible. My only other concern is that it has a number of the black keys missing, a legacy of a fall from a removal lorry. If, however, Mr Previn is as good as Roger says he is, then he should be able to overcome this minor handicap, and I am sure that he will have played on worse pianos in his jazz club days. In the afternoon we calculate that we will now be able to accommodate some eighteen chairs. Naturally Roger and myself will want to be present, which will leave us with sixteen. This number of seats multiplied by our planned price, per seat, of twenty-five guineas will bring in just over four hundred pounds, hardly a fortune, and then of course we have no guarantee that Mr André Previn's name alone will tempt this many people. Roger says we should think up some gimmick to enable us to charge more, or failing that invite somebody famous. Now that is a good idea and I know just the person: His Royal Highness, Charles, Prince of Wales. If he agrees to come then we might expand the evening's entertainment and 'bill the event', as I understand they say in show business, as a 'benefit'. Needless to say I offer the Prince and his wife complimentary tickets and the seats nearest the fire.

Tuesday, 22 November

Still enthused by thoughts of our own 'command performance', I explain to Roger that, whilst Mr Previn may be all right for the mature section of our audience, we should also cater for the younger element, who might otherwise become restive. I draw the line at popular music groups as I do not want the kitchen full of drunken groupies. Roger thinks we should ask a Kenny Everett. I must confess I have never heard of him, but Roger says he is very popular and has a strong interest in international affairs even to the extent, on one occasion, of giving advice on foreign policy to a conference of Young Conservatives. I write to ask Mr Everett what exactly it is he does, and whether he does it to music. If so we might be able to persuade Mr Previn to accompany him.

Friday, 25 November

Ingrid is still having trouble with her back. Specialist medical advice suggests that it is muscular strain caused by lifting something too heavy. I must admit I could not resist a smile when I received this news. She is disappointed that she will not now be able to take part in WAVE's fun run, intended to raise money for a South American woman accused of murdering her husband because he stepped on her flowerbed. I know how upsetting this sort of thing can be. Roger was livid when the dustmen knocked the top off the front laurel, but I think committing murder over a handful of daisies is a little extreme. Ingrid on the other hand was of the opinion that slicing him open with a machete was the least he could expect, and she said she felt sorry for the woman who was driven to this action. I do try to be as fair as possible, but on this occasion I'm afraid most of my sympathy is with the deceased. Ingrid's ears were going pink and I could see an argument developing on this point when Roger tactfully changed the subject. The United States has recently imported cruise missiles which the newspapers say are just like the old doodlebugs, but make a louder bang. However Roger's attention was drawn to another part of the article. Whereas, from what I remember, the doodle-bugs were a long way up, these new cruise missiles fly at 'tree-top height'. This is a worry because of course that is the very height of the top of our trees. If one of these cruise missiles should be on its way to, say, Leningrad, via Canterbury, and fly over 3 Cherry Drive, then it would stand a good chance of hitting one of the fruit trees. It might even strike the

Bramley apple, which has to date a very chequered history and might stop producing altogether. I think the best way out of this is to inform Mr John Stanley, the Armed Forces minister, that I am extending the ban on civil aircraft to include military ones as well as these cruise missiles.

Monday, 28 November

A Red Letter Day. It seems I have been left some money by an elderly relative. I cannot say I recall very much about Aunt Ethel other than that she married somebody in the diplomatic service and spent a lot of time doing good works in the Far East. This legacy of one thousand pounds is not quite the Nobel Prize (which I understand we have not won, it going instead to that plump little Polish man with the big moustache) but it will certainly come in useful. Our Challenger for Cherry Drive Fund now totals one thousand and six pounds, fifty-eight pence. Having never owned a battle tank before I am concerned about the regulations governing its use on public roads. I had a long chat with Mr Bridger about this when he delivered the piano, but he was no wiser than I am. He said that in his day the tanks just used to career around knocking things down and the Ministry of Defence settled up afterwards, but this is not a policy we could adopt as it would put too much of a strain on our purse-strings. I did look at the big sign at the beginning of the M2 but I find no mention of battle tanks there and I'm sure the fine for speeding in one of these vehicles would be considerable. I cannot expect Roger, who is most observant of the traffic regulations, always keeping a copy of the Highway Code in the glove compartment, to go out in traffic in our tank without cognizance of the laws relating to its use, and risk an endorsement. Do they for example need an M.O.T. certificate or have to have a minimum depth of track all over? I shall write to Mrs Lynda Chalker, the Transport Minister, for a list of do's and don't's regarding use of battle tanks on British roads; then if Roger observes these carefully he will have no need to worry.

HOUSE OF COMMONS
LONDON SWIA OAA

1 December 1983

Dear Mr Petty,

    Very many thanks for your letter of 20 November.

    I fear there is little point in writing to Dr Luns as he is now standing down as Secretary General of NATO. However, might I suggest that you contact Mr Ken Aldred of Peace Through NATO, an All-Party Group in this country which as its name implies exists to support the NATO alliance. For your information I enclose a copy of a recent speech I made at an Oxford Union debate.

    Yours sincerely,

Winston S Churchill

W Morgan Petty Esq
3 Cherry Drive
Canterbury
KENT

Friday, 2 December

A letter arrives from Mr Winston Churchill. I wrote to him
a little while ago explaining that we had followed his advice
and made inquiries to join NATO but that we had not received
a reply. I know that Dr Luns is a busy man, adding up all the
Soviet tanks and aeroplanes, or whatever else it is he does, but
seven months does seem a long delay. I therefore thought Mr
Churchill might know the Secretary General personally and
could put in a quiet word to speed things up. It seems that Dr
Luns is soon to retire, and Mr Churchill suggests instead that
we contact an organization called 'Peace Through NATO'. I
shall do this tonight. I wonder if the perks of belonging to this
are as good.

Monday, 5 December

Yesterday Roger went to the opening night of 'Cinderella's
Revenge', a seasonal pantomime performed by Ingrid's
friends from WAVE. I must say he seemed a little vague over
coffee as to exactly what it was about. I know he found the
scene where the Ugly Sisters tortured Buttons to death, described in the programme he brought back as symbolic of the
female struggle to overcome patriarchy, a bit off-putting, and
I also think he missed the traditional fairy in lamé and tulle,
her place having been taken by a young lady in leotard and
stripy socks. He confides in me that he will have a diplomatic
cold for their next production, 'Little Women'. Both he and
Mr Bridger are greatly concerned about talk of a 'Nuclear
Winter' following a thermo-nuclear exchange. Whilst they are
not sure of all the details, according to Mr Bridger this
'Nuclear Winter' could go on for months and months. The big
question then is whether the National Coal Board will be able
to maintain deliveries. As well as our domestic use of coal we
would also be faced with the problem of heating the greenhouse. In order to clarify the position I decide to write to the
Chairman, who Roger tells me is the same Ian MacGregor

with whom I corresponded when he was at British Steel. I tell him that I am sorry that that job didn't work out and wish him better luck at the Coal Board. It seems to me that we face two clear options. The first is to stockpile a great deal of coal, sufficient until retailers are again in a position to resume regular deliveries. The second – given that there are three pits very near to us – is to dig our own. I have asked Mr Mac-Gregor to consult his engineers with knowledge of this area and find out what chance Roger has of meeting our needs should he start digging with a pick and shovel down by the compost heap.

Tuesday, 6 December

I find Roger greatly agitated. It appears that, nuclear exchange or no nuclear exchange, he is uneasy about digging coal until the union position is clearer. Would he need to be a member of the National Union of Mineworkers? If so, would it be better for him to join before an attack, or have the N.U.M. made plans to recruit in Nuclear Free Zones afterwards? I shall write to Mr Scargill, as we would not like to have, as well as the obvious problems associated with nuclear devastation, mass picketing by members of his union.

Friday, 9 December

A letter arrives from Buckingham Palace. Unfortunately the Prince of Wales will not be able to join us for our musical evening as it seems his programme for the first six months of next year has already been arranged. That is very disappointing. I am just wondering who else we can invite, when Roger comes in from the garden. As usual he is never short of ideas and proposes I extend an invitation to David Frost, who is, he says, almost as famous and who he thinks actually gave the Christmas Message to the Nation one year in the late nineteen-sixties. I cannot say I remember that, but the name rings a bell, and I write straight away offering tickets on the same

BUCKINGHAM PALACE

From: The Assistant Private Secretary to H.R.H. The Prince of Wales

9th December, 1983.

Dear Mr Morgan Petty,

The Prince of Wales has asked me to thank you for your imaginative letter of 23rd November.

Unfortunately His Royal Highness has already arranged his programme for the first six month of 1984 and will not be able to accept your kind invitation.

His Royal Highness is nevertheless most grateful to you for taking the trouble to write as you did and has asked me to send you his very best wishes for the future.

Yours sincerely

David Roycroft.

W. Morgan Petty, Esq.

conditions. I just hope it means we will be able to charge as much.

Monday, 12 December

Roger receives a card from Mr Oliver. It extends seasonal greetings and a small note inside tells us that the tea shop business is progressing satisfactorily apart from one unfortunate incident involving Michael Hardiman, a rather surly customer and a tray of Devon cream horns. I did wonder, when they left, whether Master Hardiman's temperament was entirely suited to the smooth running of a tea shop. Ingrid has had to go to London to see yet another specialist about her back and will therefore miss the planned evening of feminist carols which I understand from Roger have been edited in such a way as to remove all references to men. Earlier in the week I heard her practising 'While Shepherdesses Watch Their Flocks By Night'. I must say I rather enjoyed it.

Wednesday, 14 December

Great gloom. Heavy rain has filled the foundations of the Command Bunker with water and suddenly, as if from nowhere, two ducks have appeared. Pretty as they are, I have told Roger that military necessity dictates their removal, and I gave him an order that they must be gone by lunchtime. Either he was not listening or deliberately ignored me, for when I take him his coffee they are still there. What is more he is feeding them his sandwiches. When I confront him he says that we should keep 'Hilda and Matilda', as he has christened them, within our Nuclear Free Zone, to supply us with fresh eggs after the holocaust. He may have a point. Ingrid returns from a few days away, camping with her friends at Greenham Common. I wonder if that is anywhere near the United States Air Force base? She is greatly upset, having been asked to leave a shop in nearby Newbury because she was 'smelly'. While I know Ingrid's mode of dress is not to everybody's taste (I personally find her pink boiler suit vulgar in the extreme) I cannot ever recall her smelling. Perhaps there was a mistake and she was being confused with somebody else. To cheer her up Roger and I agree to listen to all fifty-four verses of her new poem, 'The only good chauvinist is a dead one'. The things we do for a quiet life.

Thursday, 15 December

Roger and I spend the morning re-stringing the perimeter wire and replacing the baked bean tins that have fallen off in last night's heavy winds. We are just taking a break, and congratulating ourselves on a job well done, when an airliner enters our airspace. It is one of those with a bump under the front end and the pilot does not see, or chooses to ignore, Roger's attempts to attract attention. His signals with the semaphore flags Letitia Odette found in her attic are to no avail, and even when he shouted his loudest through the cardboard megaphone the aeroplane continued steadily onwards. I must admit that it was a long way up, and for that reason I cannot be sure whose it was, but Roger is adamant that it belonged to Lufthansa. I have therefore penned a strongly worded letter of protest to the Chairman of that company urging him to instruct his pilots to observe the position here. I shall also have to have another word with the Civil Aviation Authority. Roger is livid that the Squirrel was not ready (we have just finished upholstering the pilot's seat) as he says international rules require the intruder to be buzzed by aircraft from the state whose airspace has been infringed and then, if this is ignored, to force the aircraft to land. I am a little perplexed by the prospect of this latter course of action as we have nowhere big enough to accommodate a Jumbo.

Sunday, 18 December

Letitia Odette arrives to finalize plans for the holiday period. Normally Roger and I would go to them on Christmas Day and they return the visit on Boxing Day. However, given the present tense international situation, I suggest they come to us both days in case the balloon goes up. It has been our custom to go for a long walk on Boxing Day, but I have had to put my foot down and cancel this, this year. The newspapers are full of reports of missile test firings going wrong, and so I have earmarked that morning for an exercise in civil defence. What to do if by some mistake a cruise missile crash-lands in the flowerbeds? To my surprise Letitia thought this an excellent idea and has volunteered herself and Viola as helpers, making big pots of tea and singing things like 'We'll Meet Again' to keep our spirits up. She even asked Ingrid if she would like to act as our casualty, but was told that 'such a role would only reinforce the passivity shown by women in crisis situations down the ages'. Instead Ingrid has appointed herself chief ambulance-person, and now Letitia's dressmaking dummy is to be our casualty instead. Even Mr Bridger offered to help out by bringing over the branches of a dead elm to simulate debris. All in all I'm quite looking forward to this, and it will give us a good appetite for lunch.

Thursday, 22 December

Roger has had a brilliant idea. He says it came to him while watching Match of the Day on television and he has been working out all the details before mentioning it. I am not a man who takes an interest in league football, unlike Roger, who was third reserve goalkeeper for his school team, and so it comes as news to me that for the first time advertising is being allowed on players' shirts. He suggests that we might be able to persuade companies with interests in the defence industry to sponsor our defence work in a similar way. We would put their logo on T-shirts over our battledress in return for cash payments or a discount on weaponry. It is apparently quite common for such companies to sponsor football and cricket matches, and I think I can safely say that our being attacked by, and holding off, a division of crack enemy soldiers would be as exciting as anything that could be seen at Wembley or Lord's. We are somewhat restricted in who we can approach as their logo or initials will have to fit comfortably on the front of a T-shirt. Anything larger would involve us in having to turn around several times during the battle for the press, and ultimately the public, to read it all, and give the sponsors full value for their money. After a thorough search of the Yellow Pages Roger and I agree to approach I.C.I. and G.E.C. in the first instance.

Saturday, 24 December

Christmas Eve; all is still and quiet. Being the festive season we have forsaken the usual air raid precautions, with Roger stringing fairy lights up around the observation tower and along the perimeter fence. At the stroke of midnight I call him in from sentry duty and we open our presents together. I have given Roger a pair of ear muffs in camouflage green, which I am sure he will appreciate as the winter draws on, and he has presented me with a steel helmet, which he says a friend of his called Malcolm made as a project at his metalwork evening class. I have been intrigued to see what Letitia Odette has given us. She brought the somewhat large parcel round several days ago. On opening it, I find that she has knitted us a tank cosy. On a little note inside she explains that it should keep our soon-to-be-purchased fighting vehicle in superb condition until we can get the garage built. Letitia admits that she has had to guess at the size and where the barrel comes out but that she used a teapot as a model and sort of multiplied up. Looking at this tank cosy lying in the sitting room I have some doubts about its practicability; but still, it is the thought that counts.

Monday, 26 December

We had intended to hold a vitally important civil defence exercise today. However, it rained, and as neither the Odette sisters nor Mr Bridger had mackintoshes we settled for a game of Monopoly instead. Ingrid, who as chief ambulance-person was to have been in charge, was very disappointed, a mood not helped by landing in jail first time around the board and her subsequent inability to throw a double six. I take this opportunity, as we are all together, to make further plans for our musical evening. Roger says that it is very much the form on occasions like these to have a pretty girl in evening dress about the place, although for what reason he isn't sure. We give some thought to who we might ask. Ingrid says her friend Francesca from WAVE 'is very into the classics at present' and might help us out. I think I remember Francesca, or Frank as she prefers to be called, from the time she gave Ingrid a lift here. I do not think her spark-plug earrings or spiky green hair would quite set the right tone. Viola Odette suggests we invite Selina Scott, who she says is charming. Unfortunately Viola doesn't know the colour of Ms Scott's hair because they only have a black and white set. I shall drop her a line and ask whether she would wish to grace our little function, pointing out that as well as standing around looking decorative we would expect her to pop around during the intervals and sell a few ice-creams and bags of toffee. As I put the letter in the box I cross my fingers that her hair is a natural colour.

Saturday, 31 December

Publication of the New Year's Honours List, and Roger, who went straight from sentry duty to meet the mail train, is not included. I had thought that, with all the information I had given the Prime Minister and the Secretary of State about his activities over the past year (including his research with Mr Bridger to find a fall-out-resistant raspberry), they would have been able to offer him a little something for 'services to defence and horticulture'. He spends the morning sitting sullen and staring at the picture of Mr Heseltine that he cut out of the *Guardian*. Roger said at the time he thought the photograph made the Secretary of State look shifty, but I assured him that he always looked like that. He misses lunch (it was a nice rabbit stew) altogether. At four o'clock I find he has opened a bottle of potato and parsnip wine. After a few glasses he is complaining bitterly about being passed over in favour of 'failed industrialists and political has-beens'. I confess I have never seen him like this before and am worried in case he is showing signs of battle fatigue. No doubt a medal, however small, would buck him up enormously and, as I understand each party leader has the opportunity to present a list of names of people they think should be honoured, I have written to the Liberal leader, David Steel, explaining the position and asking if he can slip Roger in at the bottom of his for the Birthday Honours.

Tuesday, 3 January 1984

A letter arrives from Mr Trudeau's office in Ottawa, Canada. It is so long since I wrote to him I had entirely forgotten. Our plan then was to undertake some all-weather training, and I explained to the Canadian Prime Minister, who is probably unfamiliar with the climatic conditions of Canterbury, that we are not guaranteed annual snowfall. Thus, if we were to be attacked during a period of such weather we might be woefully under-prepared. I mentioned that Roger, who has an O-level in geography, had told me that large tracts of Canada were covered in snow all the year round, and said that as the Canadian government had granted the United States permission to use its territory for military exercises, including the testing of cruise missiles (I assume there are no apple trees), I was wondering whether they would be prepared to allow Roger and myself, with our tent and Camping Gaz, the same privilege. Now it seems that our request, after three months' delay, has been passed to the Minister of National Defence. It is a good job we are not in a hurry.

Office of the   Cabinet du
Prime Minister   Premier ministre

Ottawa, Canada
K1A 0A2

December 30, 1983.

W. Morgan Petty,
3 Cherry Drive,
Canterbury, Kent,
ENGLAND.

Dear W. Morgan Petty:

On behalf of the Prime Minister, I would like
to thank you for your letter of September 20 in which
you request permission to use Canadian territory for
your self-defence training program. I apologize for
our delay in replying.

I have taken the liberty of forwarding a copy
of your correspondence to the Office of the Honourable
Jean-Jacques Blais, Minister of National Defence.

I trust this will ensure that the matter you
have raised will be given full consideration.

Yours sincerely,

S. K.

for Edward J. Gorecki,
Correspondence Assistant.

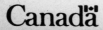

Thursday, 5 January

Ingrid arrives to cheer Roger up. He has been complaining of stomach pains and I have made him a bed up on the sofa. It may be a psychosomatic symptom of his depression, or more likely the richness of Viola Odette's cheese dip on New Year's Eve. In any event Ingrid says she knows just the thing and produces a rather evil-smelling jar from her string bag. In it, she tells us, is a recipe from a seventeenth-century book of witchcraft. Both Roger and myself are a little startled by this. I have always regarded witches as rather nasty individuals, covering people with warts and trying to do away with Dorothy's dog in *The Wizard of Oz*, but, according to Ingrid, they were rather more a Mystical Sisterhood, a sort of Middle Ages Women's Institute, who did a bit of healing on the side and to whom history has not been kind. I cannot say this secret recipe seems to have done Roger any good. Admittedly he did get up this afternoon, but I think that this was occasioned more by the threat of hearing one of Ingrid's epic poems than by any miracle cure.

Friday, 6 January

I wake to find that overnight someone has crashed into the back of the Morris Minor and driven off without leaving a name and address. Fortunately the damage is not very bad and some T-Cut and elbow grease should remove the worst. Roger still being laid up, I ask Mr Bridger to attend to this. I am only thankful that it was not the Challenger that was parked outside; according to Mr Bridger, battle tanks have to be kept in excellent condition to retain their value, the second-hand market in them being a bit slow. He asks whether our insurance on the Morris Minor can be extended to cover the Challenger. I must say I had not given this much thought, and it would certainly be as well to clarify the position before we take delivery. It might also be as well, given the highly competitive nature of the insurance business, to get some comparative premiums. I have therefore written to Mr Peter North-Miller, the Chairman at Lloyds of London, asking for a quotation for fully comprehensive and third party, fire and theft cover on the Challenger, and his suggestions and ideas on the sort of insurance we might want for the Squirrel. I must also remember to ask what day of the week he comes to collect the money.

Saturday, 7 January

It seems yet another report about the climatic conditions prevailing after a nuclear war has been published. Unlike the one which anticipates a 'Nuclear Winter', this one suggests that the planet will be left sub-tropical. I just wish they would make up their minds. Naturally we must, as a fighting unit, prepare a response for whatever weather conditions we may find ourselves in. The 'Nuclear Winter' will be adequately taken care of by the anticipated favourable response of the Canadian government allowing us to use their frozen wastes. But the question of tropical training might prove more difficult. Roger suggested curtly that we spend a few weeks up the Amazon. I am not sure whether in his present mood he was being sarcastic, and anyway we could not spare the time just now. It was then that I had an idea which I thought might solve this problem and snap Roger out of what I fear is becoming a self-pitying mood. We would hold the tropical exercises in the garden greenhouse. My idea was to stoke up the heater, turn the gauge to maximum and send Roger in. Unfortunately when we tried this he went all blotchy in the heat and has complained of headaches ever since. He said, after coming round, that this had not been the brightest of my ideas, or words to very similar effect. I still think the basic principle is sound: all we need is a bigger greenhouse (ours is only eight foot by six). I have therefore written to Professor Bell, the Director of Kew Gardens, to see if he will let us use one of his for our counter-insurgency training. I tell him that anywhere with a few Monstera Deliciosa or Ficus Elastica will do, and that because of the nature of the exercise and all the glass, we will not bring our tank.

Sunday, 8 January

Ingrid arrives. Rather sheepishly she explains that in her haste to prepare her concoction from the witches' book of spells and potions she turned over two pages at once and, whilst she followed the first half of the recipe for curing an upset stomach faithfully, the latter stages were of a mixture for clearing infection from sheep's feet. No wonder Roger felt so bad. Still, he seems on the mend now, and I suggest to Ingrid that this little mistake remain a secret between us, and joke that at least she has cleared up Roger's foot-rot. Unfortunately she does not seem to see the funny side of it. This incident reminds me that we have still not received advice from the Health Minister, Kenneth Clarke, about National Health provisions after a nuclear exchange, and I resolve to deal with BUPA on this matter direct. If they are unable to provide us with a post-nuclear scheme and the National Health Service is in the disarray some claim it will be, then we shall be left to our own devices. Neither Roger nor myself very much likes the idea of removing the other's appendix, but needs must, and so I have approached Geoffrey Slaney, President of the Royal College of Surgeons, to see how we might go about it. Perhaps we could join his college for a course of lessons, or maybe he himself could give us a few written instructions about which organs might be in the way after the initial incision and the best way to avoid them. I apologize to Professor Slaney for bothering him with this matter. Roger had suggested that we use Dr Jonathan Miller's pop-up book on *The Human Body* as our guideline, but unfortunately it was so popular that W. H. Smith's had sold out. Perhaps everybody else has the same idea.

Imperial Chemical Industries PLC

Imperial Chemical House
Millbank London SW1P 3JF

Telephone 01-834 4444

From
D S Hay
General Manager –
Commercial

11 January 84

W Morgan Petty Esq
3 Cherry Drive
Canterbury
Kent

Dear Mr Morgan Petty

I am responding to your letter dated 22 December 83, but postmarked
9 January 84, addressed to the Chairman of ICI.

Your individualistic approach to matters that cause you concern is
interesting. However, our central sponsorship kitty is currently in even
worse shape than your Defence Fund, being empty, so I am sorry we will not
be able to help.

Yours sincerely

Stuart Hay

Registered in England No. 218019 Registered Office Imperial Chemical House Millbank London SW1P 3JF

A letter arrives from I.C.I. Unfortunately they say they are unable to help us with sponsorship as their kitty is bare. This is a terrible shame but, providing nothing dramatic happens, I have made a note to get an application in to them very early in the next financial year. Roger and I have an exciting and full day practising taking off and landing the Squirrel. We have not of course completed its construction as yet – there are still technical and materials problems, not to mention finance – but that is no reason for us not to prepare ourselves. We strapped the seat to Roger who, arms outstretched, ran around the garden simulating engine noises. All in all I found it very realistic and the exercise, as intended, produced some very useful results. For a start we have discovered that the Squirrel, because of its design for tight turns within the confines of our airspace, is very vulnerable to an attack from the rear. What we need therefore is some armour plating for behind the pilot's seat. (Currently there are three layers of Bacofoil, but neither of us has much faith in that deflecting enemy fire.) Whilst we are collecting quite a nice pile of scrap metal to build the Squirrel (only last week we acquired two old bicycle frames), we do not have any armour plating. Roger says it is not the sort of thing people throw away, and suggests that we approach the Imperial War Museum to find out whether amongst their immense collection of wartime memorabilia they have any armour plating they don't want. I write straight away. The second problem our exercise shows up is the limitations of our runway area. What I am concerned about is the prospect of an overshoot. If the prevailing wind should be to the north, then the Squirrel would end up on the patio, with heaven knows what damage. Should the prevailing wind be to the south, then the Squirrel risks landing in the anti-tank ditch behind the rhododendron bush and demolishing a section of shiplap fencing. Roger says that he was watching a film on television, I think it starred John Wayne, where planes were landing on the deck of an aircraft carrier and were stopped from crashing over the side by giant elastic bands. This is of course just what we need to stop our own aircraft from overshooting. I have therefore also dropped a line to Sir Ian Gilmour, the former minister responsible for the navy, asking where they buy these big elastic bands and approximately how much they cost.

Tuesday, 17 January

I receive a letter from Sarah Cullen at Independent Television News. After John Pilger's reply to our invitation to accompany us on manoeuvres went astray in the post, Roger, strongly supported by Ingrid, insisted that our next invitation be extended to a female journalist, thus avoiding our being labelled 'sexist'. As I was sure that a woman would make a much better job of cooking on the one ring of our Camping Gaz, I agreed. I made it clear, however, to Ms Cullen that given the parlous state of our finances she would have to supply her own kit. Unfortunately she is unable to accept, but in her letter does provide one valuable piece of information. It seems that you can buy crystals which stop salt from going solid. I think the aspect of warfare that I dread most is not the blood, the discomfort or the mangled bodies but having a blocked-up salt-cellar when in possession of a crispy piece of celery. In the afternoon we extend the Squirrel programme to include parachute jumping. I expect that our aircraft will prove excellent in performance, but we must be prepared for the worst. It may even be that some other eagle-eyed warrior of the sky might 'shoot it up', causing Roger to bale out. The Odette sisters have run him up a very nice 'chute from some old bed-linen and he has been practising 'target jumping' from the Bramley apple. Unfortunately whilst he was trying a particularly difficult descent on to the cross I had whitewashed on the lawn, his guide ropes got tangled up on an overhanging branch, and he took a nasty tumble. I am glad to report that he has nothing more than a bruised knee, but I think his parachute is a write-off.

Independent Television News Limited ITN House, 48 Wells Street, London W1P 4DE
Registered office

Phone: 01-637 2424
Telex: 22101
Cables: Telindep, London PS4
Registered number 548648 England

16th January 1984

W. Morgan Petty
3 Cherry Drive
Canterbury
Kent

Dear Sir

Thank you for your most interesting letter.

I am fascinated by your plans for the nuclear free zone
at 3 Cherry Drive, but I cannot quite understand why it
should also be necessary to conduct manoeuvres outside it?

I must admit to being offended initially by being only your
third choice of journalist, but on reflection I decided
Hastings and Pilger are fairly substantial competition!
I am glad to note that you seem to have no political bias
in your choice of reporter. However, much as I would like
to accept your invitation, I am afraid military matters are
outside my province as Home Affairs Correspondent; and
professional ethics force me to decline. May I suggest that
your invitation might be better addressed to Geoffrey Archer,
ITN's Defence Correspondent?

Yours sincerely

Sarah Cullen

ps If you go to your nearest camping shop you can buy a sachet
    of crystals which will stop your salt from going solid!

Directors
Lord Buxton (Chairman). Alastair Burnet. Bryan Cowgill. Paul Fox. William Hodgson. Alex Mair. David McCall. Paul McKee. Daniel Moloney. David Nicholas (Editor).
Peter Paine. Robert Phillis. David Plowright. Brian Tesler.

Wednesday, 18 January

Roger's knee is extremely badly swollen. When Ingrid arrives she asks if we would like her to look up a cure in her book of spells and potions. I decline the offer. I think Roger is upset not so much by his discomfort as by the dashed hopes of his running a sponsored marathon to raise money for the Defence Fund. Ingrid suggests that he might undertake another sponsored activity, something he is really good at. I must admit the silence was quite embarrassing, and I was grateful when Mr Bridger, who had popped in with a couple of black keys for the piano his brother Arthur found while clearing out his shed, suggested a sponsored sentry duty. The plan would be for Roger to stand guard for seven days and seven nights, and in such a situation his bad knee would not matter at all. I must say we all thought this an excellent idea. All, that is to say, except Roger, who suggested that the sentry duty last only four days. I think it was a bit mean of Mr Bridger to have called him a spoilsport, and Ingrid even offered, 'in the cause of equality', to stand guard with him. Happily she discovered a prior engagement reading her new poem 'Romance enslaves women and turns them from the fundamental realization of their own abilities to live a life overshadowed by male values', which, she tells us proudly, contains seventy-two verses and which, with discussion, she anticipates lasting four hours. When she has gone Roger says that he sometimes wonders whether Ingrid judges her poems more by length than substance, but I am more left wondering what she will rhyme with such a long first line. In the second post we receive another letter from Canada. It is from the office of the Minister of National Defence, telling us that our request will be brought to the minister's attention at the earliest opportunity. After this length of time I am beginning to think we might have done better to hire an ice-rink.

16 January 1984

Mr. W. Morgan Petty
3 Cherry Drive
Canterbury, Kent
ENGLAND

Dear Mr. Petty:

On behalf of the Honourable Jean-Jacques Blais, I would like to acknowledge your letter dated 20 September 1983, addressed to the Prime Minister, requesting permission to use Canadian territory for your self-defence training program.

Please be assured that your request will be brought to the Minister's attention at the earliest opportunity.

Sincerely,

C.R. Thibault
Lieutenant-Colonel
Minister's Staff Officer

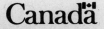

Thursday, *19 January*

This morning finds me writing letters to potential sponsors for
Roger's sentry duty. I am only asking the enormously rich,
whose names we have taken from the financial pages of the
Guardian. Amongst those I have approached are Richard
Giordano, the Chief Executive of British Oxygen, who is
apparently the highest paid person in the country, and Nigel
Broackes, who owns the QE2. I am hopeful that people in this
income bracket will consider a figure of one hundred pounds
an hour; with enough sponsors of this kind, we stand a good
chance of raising the money for the Challenger's turret. Roger,
who did a national certificate in accountancy some years ago,
suggested that people are, as he put it, 'more likely to lay some
bread on us' if they think they can get a similar amount
allowed against income tax. It seems that one of the simplest
ways of doing this would be for our Nuclear Free Zone to
become a registered charity. I have therefore made some
initial inquiries of the Charity Commission as to how we go
about obtaining that status. I warn Roger against being too
optimistic, but, as he points out, the Commission have in the
past given charitable status to some very dubious bodies, and
a fine upright defence organization like ourselves ought to
qualify for at least as much consideration. A letter has arrived
from the National Coal Board. They are not convinced that
Roger would be successful digging our own coal and suggest
the stockpiling option instead. Given the uncertainty as to the
length of this 'Nuclear Winter' I suppose we ought to get in
at least three tons, though heaven knows where we will put it.

Saturday, *21 January*

Roger is getting on very well with the Squirrel. He has made
the canopy out of an old plastic garden cloche. Now, with the
pilot's seat strapped to him, the cloche over his head, and his
silk scarf trailing behind, things are really beginning to take
shape. It is therefore time to give some thought to his flying

TELEPHONE
01-235 2020

TELEX 882161 HOB

NATIONAL COAL BOARD
HOBART HOUSE
GROSVENOR PLACE
LONDON SW1X 7AE

Our Ref. AD 84/9   17th January, 1984

W. Morgan Petty, Esq.,
3 Cherry Drive,
Canterbury,
Kent.

Dear Mr. Petty,

    Mr. MacGregor has asked me to thank you for your recent letter
about how to heat your greenhouses in the event of nuclear attack.
I am replying on his behalf.

    Whilst it must be right to consider the possibilities of damage
in such circumstances (even in a nuclear free zone such as your own)
it is very difficult to offer you specific advice. We very much hope
there will be no nuclear attack but, if there is, greenhouses will,
I am afraid, be particularly vulnerable. The prospects of resuming
coal supplies will depend on the severity of the attack.

    Of the two options you mention I would recommend that you prefer
that of stockpiling coal. With the equipment you describe Roger
could not dig deep enough to reach any coal there may be under your
garden.

                              Yours sincerely,

                              P. N. Moullin
                              Deputy Secretary

lessons. He has already been practising what I think is called 'in-flight simulation' with a kitchen chair, some blocks of wood, and a copy of *Teach Yourself Subsonic Aviation*. I must say Roger is quite prepared to learn to fly by means of trial and error, although I am not too keen on this approach, fearing too much error might cause damage both to him and to the greenhouse. We certainly cannot afford the prices that are being charged by flying schools, and Mr Bridger suggested we look for a former R.A.F. type who might give up a few hours of his time to teach Roger the basics. By coincidence I read only yesterday that Lord Trefgarne, the Parliamentary Under-Secretary of State at the Ministry of Defence, was in his time an airman of some note and received a Royal Aero Club Bronze Medal for a record-breaking flight between England and Australia. I have therefore written to ask if, when he gets a couple of days off from what I am sure is a very important job, he would like to come down and give Roger some hints. In return I shall ask Viola Odette if she will lay on one of her special high teas.

Monday, 23 January

It is as I feared: BUPA do not offer a post-nuclear scheme, and I find Lord Wigoder's reply to my letter somewhat depressing. It is sad to think of all those radiantly happy couples, with their two-and-a-half children, not having, when they really need it most, the opportunity to avail themselves of private hospital facilities. In the same post is a letter from Selina Scott. She says she will be unable to attend our musical evening as her diary is too full up. This is such a shame as I never did find out what colour her hair was.

Wednesday, 25 January

I am very disappointed that we have not had a reply from the United States Military Academy at West Point. I have always regarded Americans as extremely efficient people, or, as Roger

Head Office

Provident House
Essex Street
London WC2R 3AX

Telephone: 01-353 9451
Telex: 883059

BTW/JAG/AW

W. Morgan Petty, Esq.,
3, Cherry Drive,
Canterbury,
Kent.

BUPA

19th January, 1984.

Dear Mr. Morgan Petty,

Thank you for your most interesting letter of 9th January.

I am sorry to have to tell you that the Association possesses neither the formidable armoury that you are fortunate enough to own nor, to defend us from fall-out problems, any privet hedges. The lack of the latter is true not only of Head Office but of every one of BUPA's Branches and the surrounding terrain is not conducive to the planting of them at this stage.

In the event of a nuclear attack, those of us who remain - if any - will continue to provide our service to those of our subscribers who manage to do likewise; whether the facilities necessary for their treatment will still exist, however, must be a matter for conjecture.

As an illness such as chronic catarrh is one which is normally treated by a patient's general practitioner, that treatment would not, under present circumstances, form an eligible claim on BUPA and the same might well be true in the future, even if the conditioned worsened. The removal of an appendix would be likely to form an eligible claim, but you would probably need an expert medical opinion as to whether post nuclear conditions might cause the onset of symptoms.

As you will see from the enclosed brochure, Rule 5(4) does enable us to withhold or restrict payments in the circumstances you describe and I think there is little I can do but to wish both you and Roger long life and good health.

Yours sincerely,

Lord Wigoder Q.C.
Chairman

The British United Provident Association Limited   Registered in England No. 432511
Registered Office: Provident House Essex Street London WC2R 3AX

BBC tv

BRITISH BROADCASTING CORPORATION
LIME GROVE STUDIOS LONDON W12 7RJ
TELEPHONE 01-743 8000 TELEX: 265781
TELEGRAMS AND CABLES: TELECASTS LONDON TELEX

19th January 1984

Mr W Morgan Petty
3 Cherry Drive
Canterbury
Kent

Dear Morgan Petty

How very kind of you and Roger to ask me to
your musical evening. Unfortunately, I am
in pretty much the same position as David Frost
in that my diary is too full to be believed.

I am sure you will understand. Thank you for
thinking of me. Have a happy musical evening.

Yours sincerely

Selina Scott
Breakfast Time

puts it, 'individuals with immediate response and dynamic activity patterns'. I suppose it is always possible that their reply has gone astray in the post. According to Ingrid, King's College in London have a Department of War Studies. I must say this is news to me, but she is quite certain and says she had a friend who was turned down for a place on this course, not being academically gifted. (He had to become a barrister instead.) I wonder what a Department of War Studies does? Roger thought they might give lectures and seminars to their students on how to go out and conquer other countries, but surely that can't be right. I suggest to a Lawrence Freedman, who is Professor of these War Studies, that, when the weather is warmer, he might like to bring a group of his students down to see how things are done at the sharp end of the military business, explaining that Roger and myself would be only too happy to give them a glimpse of the hardships of military life. We could also throw in some useful hints like not forgetting to take a box of matches on manoeuvres. We did, and were unable to light the Camping Gaz until we managed to borrow a box of Bryant and May's from an itinerant rambler, only to discover that we had left the tea bags behind as well. The men in the party might even be able to give Roger a hand digging our new defensive trench whilst the young ladies, if there should be any, could busy themselves in the kitchen making tea and sandwiches. It would also be a good opportunity for Professor Freedman to tell us about the content of his course; then, if we are interested, and Sir Keith Joseph supplies us with student grants, we can put our names down for next year.

Thursday, 26 January

Two letters this morning. The first is from the Royal Botanic Gardens, Kew. The Director informs me that the terms of his appointment preclude the use of the gardens for military exercises. This is a great shame as I am positive that, after his last experience, Roger will not undertake any more sub-tropical exercises in our own greenhouse. The second letter is

ROYAL BOTANIC GARDENS
KEW, RICHMOND, SURREY
01-940-1171

W Morgan Petty, Esq.
3 Cherry Drive
Canterbury
Kent.

20 January 1984

Dear Mr Petty

Thank you for your letter of 9 January.

I'm afraid that the terms under which I accepted
responsibility for the Royal Botanic Gardens preclude
their use for military exercises.

Yours sincerely

Professor E A Bell
Director

SHEFFIELD CITY COUNCIL

Councillor D. Blunkett
Leader
Sheffield City Council

Leader's Office
Town Hall
SHEFFIELD
S1 2HH   Tel. 734101

DB/CS   24th January 1984

W. Morgan Petty,
3 Cherry Drive,
Canterbury,
Kent

Dear W. Morgan Petty,

You have lightened what might otherwise be a drab and
often far too serious political environment in which
I find myself. I enjoyed your letter enormously and
wondered whether you would consider joining me in a
chorous of Land of Hope and Glory on 'Thats Life'.
With my greatest respects to Roger.

Yours in complete solidarity

DAVID BLUNKETT
Leader of the Council

from Mr David Blunkett, the leader of Sheffield City Council. I approached Mr Blunkett, along with some others, with a view to holding a cultural exchange. I must say he sounds a jolly young man, and whilst he is not specific, I think the answer is affirmative. He suggests I join him in a chorus of 'Land of Hope and Glory' on *That's Life*, which Roger says is a television programme presented by a woman with big teeth, and which consists almost entirely of singing dogs. I do hope Mr Blunkett wasn't being rude.

Saturday, 28 January

The coal man calls to deliver our order. He apologizes for being late but says that the erratic numbering on the houses in Cherry Drive caused him to call at three others first. I must say this is extremely worrying. Delivering a consignment of coal to the wrong house is one thing, but delivering a cruise or ss 20 missile to the wrong address is quite another. I spend the afternoon pondering on this, and despite Roger's assurance that the Super Powers will undoubtedly be aware of the disparity in the numbering of the houses here, and will in any case check with the diagrams we supplied to them before launching a strike, I am not convinced. I would feel happier if our nuclear free status were defined clearly on the maps that they are likely to use to prepare a nuclear attack. I have therefore written to the Director of the Ordnance Survey asking him to make this minor adjustment when they next update their plans. The afternoon post brings a letter from the Department of Transport. This lists the regulations for the use of vehicles on the road. As far as I can see there is no specific mention of battle tanks, and I find this rather surprising, as it would surely be very silly to have the same rules governing our Challenger and somebody else's Ford Granada. I know this rather vague information will not put Roger's mind at rest.

JAW/K

DEPARTMENT OF TRANSPORT

Room   C19/04
2 Marsham Street London SW1P 3EB

Telex 22221   Direct line 01-
                                Switchboard 01-212 3434
                                        GTN 212

Mr W Morgan Petty   Your reference
3 Cherry Drive
CANTERBURY   Our reference
Kent   532/5
                                     Date
                                     27 January 1984

Dear Mr Morgan Petty

1. Thank you for your letter of 1 December 1983 to the Minister of State for
Transport, Mrs Chalker. I have been asked to reply.

2. The principal legislation governing the use of vehicles both wheeled and
tracked on the road are the Road Traffic Regulation Act 1967, the Road Traffic
Act 1972 and the Regulations made under these Acts. These include the Motor
Vehicles (Construction and Use) Regulations 1978, the Motor Vehicles (Construction
and Use) (Track laying vehicles) Regulations 1955 and the Road Vehicles Lighting
Regulations 1971.

3. Copies of these Acts and Regulations can be obtained from HMSO and may be
available in some libraries. I should point out, however, that the legislation
has been amended considerably, for example there have been more than 30 amendments
to the Construction and Use Regulations.

Yours sincerely

Ian Davis

IAN DAVIS
Vehicle Standards and Engineering Division (4)

Monday, 30 January

Letitia Odette confirms that our parachute is beyond repair.
She has offered to run us up another one, but there is a
problem: the only sheets she has left are some she bought at
a jumble sale and these are, unfortunately, covered with
Disney characters. She tells me that even though she has dyed
them orange Donald and Pluto are clearly visible. I am not
sure that a parachute of this nature is quite the sort of thing
a crack fighting unit like ourselves should be using, and I have
therefore written to that very helpful Major Martin in the
Parachute Regiment to ask if they have any secondhand ones,
as I know how anxious Roger is to continue his training.

Wednesday, 1 February

I receive two letters. The first is from the office of the Director
General of the Ordnance Survey. Unfortunately he regrets he
is unable to meet our request. We shall therefore have to hope
and pray that the Super Powers are very careful in setting the
co-ordinates for their nuclear strikes. The second is from Sir
Ian Gilmour. It seems that he has been giving a great deal of
thought to our plea for help but has decided finally that to
supply us with the information we require about big elastic
bands might breach the Official Secrets Act. Naturally I
understand his position and would not wish to compromise
him. Still, it is a nuisance. I shall have to think of someone else
to approach or, if we can get a length of rubber hose ourselves,
perhaps Roger might have a go at making one.

Friday, 3 February

Letitia and Viola have suggested that, as the first anniversary
of my declaring 3 Cherry Drive a Nuclear Free Zone ap-
proaches, we should think of marking it in some way. I must
say this is a splendid idea. I do not think however that it should
be a very elaborate affair – just a few close friends and the odd

ORDNANCE SURVEY
Romsey Road Maybush Southampton SO9 4DH

Telephone 0703 (Southampton) 775555 ext
   GTN 2027

National Grid Reference SU 387148

W Morgan Petty *Esq*.
3 Cherry Drive
CANTERBURY
Kent

Your reference

Our reference IE/M/84

Date 31 January 1984

Dear Mr Morgan Petty

The Director General has asked me to acknowledge and
thank you for your letter of 26 January 1984.

He regrets that he is unable to meet your request.

Yours sincerely

PAUL WATTS
Information Branch

From: The Rt. Hon. Sir Ian Gilmour, Bt., M.P.

HOUSE OF COMMONS
LONDON SWIA OAA

31st January 1984

Dear Mr Morgan Petty,

Many thanks for your interesting and
entertaining letter.   I am sorry I haven't answered it
before but I have been giving the matter deep thought and
making a number of enquiries.

I am afraid the result of both these processes is
a decision that I am unable to give you the information
you ask for because I believe to do so would be contrary
to the Official Secrets Act.

Yours sincerely,

W. Morgan Petty Esq.,
3 Cherry Drive,
Canterbury,
Kent.

international statesman. I explain to Roger my intention of inviting Mrs Thatcher. She has, of late, acquired something of a bellicose image. I am sure that she is not at all like that really. When I was much younger I went out several times with a young lady called Miranda who also hailed from Grantham. She was the most charming of creatures and not aggressive in the least – a trait which I assumed to be characteristic of the area. I cannot believe Mrs Thatcher to be as stubborn and warlike as some people claim. I have therefore dropped a little note to Bernard Ingham, her press secretary. I am sure she would enjoy the company and Viola Odette's vol-au-vents and, should she be able to persuade Fleet Street to cover her visit, an appearance amongst such obviously peace-loving people as ourselves could do a lot for her image.

Saturday, 4 February

An extraordinary day. Roger spends the morning working on the undercarriage of the Squirrel; fortunately a friend whose Lambretta was written off in a crash has let him have both tyres for five pounds. Over coffee we discuss ways of reducing the production costs on our aircraft which, on re-calculation, are now down to one hundred and ninety-five thousand pounds and sixty-eight pence. Roger, who has an O-level in economics, tells me that it would actually be cheaper to build two Squirrels rather than one. It is, he says, something to do with 'economies of scale'. I must confess that I am very sceptical, for if building two Squirrels means they cost less, then, logically, building hundreds means they wouldn't cost anything at all. Roger agrees that it may be nonsense but it is, he says, sound economics, and to substantiate this appears with one of the old textbooks from his evening class. We resolve therefore to build two Squirrels, but are left with the problem of what to do with the other one. However much I would like to fly as Roger's 'wingman' I have no head for heights, and so I have approached Geoffrey Pattie to see if he would like to purchase our 'spare' for the R.A.F. Given that it is being conceived, designed and built by Roger, I have no doubt that it will be the equal of anything currently in service, and of course should we manage to sell it the revenue would greatly boost our Defence Fund.

Monday, 6 February

Yesterday evening, after the usual late patrol of our borders, Roger and myself settle down, with our cocoa and biscuits, to watch the news. Unfortunately the reception on BBC 1 and BBC 2 is once again terrible. The picture is distinctly fuzzy around the edges and the colour has gone very pale. (Poor Michael Fish, the weather man, looked positively anaemic earlier in the week.) At first I thought the starlings had taken to building nests on our aerial again, but a quick search revealed nothing. Roger says he wonders whether President Reagan blowing up a satellite in outer space with a rocket has anything to do with it. I confess that this is the first I have heard of this action but, according to Roger, the news was all over the international pages of the *Guardian*. I tell him that, *Guardian* or not, he must be mistaken, as something like that would clearly be in breach of international law; but Roger asks what else you could expect from a 'warmongering geriatric'. I think he probably got that from the *Guardian* as well. I harbour the sneaking suspicion that the television set itself may be on the blink, but blowing up satellites cannot be helping matters. I have therefore dropped a short note to the President asking for his opinion. As someone who was once connected with the entertainment industry, I am sure he will view my concerned inquiry sympathetically. I have also asked him to suspend any more violent activity in outer space until we know the cause of the television's problem for definite. I dread to think what would happen if he were to blow up another satellite and Channel Four was to suffer, as Roger has been instructed by Ingrid to watch a series on female sexuality which is only partly through, and he is sure she is going to set him some sort of test at the end.

Charity Commission
14 Ryder Street St James's London SW1Y 6AH

Telephone Direct line 01-214⎫
GTN   214⎬ 8470
Switchboard 01 214 6000⎭

W Morgan Petty Esq
3 Cherry Drive
Canterbury
Kent

Your reference

Our reference
RH-147967(1533)-R
Date
2 February 1984

Dear Mr Petty

Thank you for your letter of 25 January outlining your proposals for establishing a
new charity. It is very heartening to know that there are still dedicated and
patriotic people who are willing to devote their energies to extending the boundaries
of voluntary effort.

As you may be aware, the essence of charity is altruism and public benefit and any
organisation which seeks to be registered as a charity must contain these two
ingredients. I suppose that to relieve the Ministry of Defence of some of the burden
of international defence might be regarded as altruistic but it appears that apart
from you the only other beneficiary of your activities will be your colleague Roger
and unfortunately that is too narrow a section of the public to satisfy the second
test.

I hope that you will not be too disappointed by this response. Sometimes we do have
to reject applications from organisations which are eminently worthy but which do not
meet the legal requirements for registration as a charity.

I should like to end on a more personal note. It occurs to me that even after all
your fund-raising efforts you may not have sufficient cash to purchase a Challenger
tank. If that is the case may I suggest that you ask the obviously versatile Roger
to turn his hand to inventing: I understand that many varied and useful articles have
been made out of old petrol-driven lawn mowers which can often be bought cheaply at
garden centres.

With all best wishes to you and Roger for the sponsored Sentry Duty.

Yours sincerely

R HATTON

THE RT. HON. DAVID STEEL. M.P.

HOUSE OF COMMONS
LONDON SWIA OAA

6th February 1984

Dear Mr Petty,

    Thank you for your letter of 31st December about the
sterling work of your part-time gardener, Roger. I understand
his irritation at being passed over, but I'm afraid you will
have to direct your request to the Prime Minister.
Recommendations for services to defence and horticulture do
not come within my remit.

    My task is simply to recommend a small number of people
each year who give outstanding service to politics. From what
you say of all Roger's activities, it does not sound as though
he would have much time to devote to this other activity.

    However, please pass on my warm appreciation of all that
he does.

Yours sincerely,

W. Morgan Petty
3 Cherry Drive
CANTERBURY
Kent

Wednesday, 8 February

Two disappointing missives arrive today. The first is from the Charity Commission. Unfortunately we do not appear to come within their terms of reference and cannot therefore claim charitable status. This will greatly disappoint Roger who has, in anticipation, already made a number of collecting boxes and a flag cushion. The second is from the Liberal leader, David Steel. He too is the bearer of bad news. It appears that as leader of his party he can only recommend honours for people with service in politics. Roger did once go to the hustings, for the council elections, on a really blustery and wet night, but I suppose that doesn't count.

Friday, 10 February

A letter arrives from Professor Freedman at King's College, which I read to Roger and Mr Bridger whilst they are preparing the shallots for sowing. It seems the purpose of this War Studies course is to explore war as a phenomenon. Blank looks all round. He also somewhat chastises us for what he describes as a 'sexist' presumption that females are better for nothing more than 'tea and sandwiches'. Oh dear, we do seem to have got off on the wrong foot. Perhaps I should drop him a short note explaining about Ingrid's back. I just hope that if we do eventually undertake his course he won't hold this little misunderstanding against us and give us detention.

Wednesday, 15 February

Excitement mounts as we approach the celebrations for our first anniversary. I have not heard from Mrs Thatcher yet, nor Mr Reagan, who I also invited to attend. Mr Bridger has built a huge bonfire which he plans to light on the 22nd. He says he wants it to be just like the one he built for the Queen's Silver Jubilee. I personally hope that it's not exactly the same, for on that occasion his bonfire tumbled over and burned down

King's College London

Strand, London WC2R 2LS

Telephone 01-836 5454

Department of War Studies

Professor Lawrence Freedman

7 February 1984

Dear Mr Petty,

Thank you for your letter of 25 January. I am somewhat surprised
that, having taken over responsibility for your own security, you now wish
to employ mercenaries. I am also concerned at the sexist presumption that
our 'females' are better for nothing more than tea and sandwiches.

I'm afraid we do not train our students to participate in
conquest but to explore war as a phenomenon. As someone of your military
experience would be an undoubted asset on our course I enclose a prospectus.
Roger may find it instructive as well.

I wish you luck with your nuclear-free zone. Since Mr Livingstone
declared one in London not a single nuclear weapon has been detonated over
the capital.

Yours sincerely,

Mr W. Morgan Petty,
3, Cherry Drive,
CANTERBURY,
Kent.

Enc

From: Major Philip NEAME PARA

REGIMENTAL HEADQUARTERS,
THE PARACHUTE REGIMENT,
BROWNING BARRACKS,
ALDERSHOT,
HAMPSHIRE.

Aldershot Military } Ext. 4621
G.P.O. : Aldershot 24431 }

MS8

W Morgan Petty
3 Cherry Drive
Canterbury
Kent

14 February 1984

Dear Mr Morgan Petty,

Thank you for your letter of 30 January to Major Martin, which has
been passed to me in his absence. I am pleased to hear that you
found the advice of such an erstwhile colleague useful.

Regrettably, we are unable to offer any secondhand parachutes for sale.
All military parachutes are handled by the RAF, who guard them like
gold dust, since we as a Regiment have found them invaluable for
tailoring into tracksuits and bivouac bags. If ever one does fall
off the back of a lorry, there are already dozens of eager takers!

I hope Roger's knees have now recovered. The accident must have
given him quite a turn. Personally, I would rather enjoy coming down
under a fresco of Donald Duck and Pluto (far more up-lifting than
olive green), and believe you should encourage the Odettes with their
kind offer.

However, if you really feel that is not good enough, you could always
try tapping the RAF . . . I hope you have better luck than us!

Yours sincerely
Philip Neame

From: **David St J Beaty, Private Secretary**

MINISTRY OF DEFENCE

WHITEHALL LONDON SW1A 2HB

Telephone 01- 218 6621 (Direct Dialling)
01-218 9000 (Switchboard)

Minister of State
for Defence Procurement

D/MIN/GP/14/1

8 February 1984

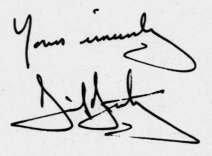

Mr Pattie has asked me to thank you for your letter of 2nd February, the contents of which he has noted.

W Morgan Petty Esq

MINISTRY OF DEFENCE

Main Building, Whitehall, London SWIA 2HB

Telephone (Direct Dialling) 01-218

(Switchboard) 01-218 9000

Reference: 3/1/1/1   20 February 1984

W Morgan Petty Esq
3 Cherry Drive
Canterbury
Kent

Dear Mr Petty,

Lord Trefgarne has asked me to say how delighted he was to receive
your letter of 19 January, and to inform you that in view of your
singular determination to maintain credible deterrence against
aggression in the territory of KENT, you have been selected as one of
those who may be lucky beneficiaries of a unique trial of equipment
designed to convince a potential aggressor that he would indeed be
foolish to contemplate an attack on 3 CHERRY DRIVE, Canterbury,

We may be able to offer, subject to operational availability:

      i)   a trial airship for a period of several minutes to
provide unrivalled airborne early warning of an attack on
3 Cherry Drive (all this requires is an easy-to-erect 10,000m^2
hangar in your garden).

      ii)   a special nuclear deterrent screen provided by our first
Trident submarine, subject to our intrepid submariners' ability
to navigate the River STOUR.

      iii)   a special reinforcement exercise of Cherry Drive by our
newly enhanced 5th Airborne Brigade, subject to our ability
to remove an ecclesiastical edifice in Canterbury which is an
unfortunate navigational obstacle to parachute drop aircraft.

We are delighted too that you are anxious to obtain a Challenger tank
for deterrence. We are pleased to say that you, Mr MORGAN PETTY may
yet be the lucky host for a Regiment of these space age peacekeepers,
stationed in the garden of 3 Cherry Drive, and conveniently located
for swift intervention in any attempt by Gallic lorry drivers to
block the new Channel Tunnel (which may shortly break the surface
beside 3 Cherry Drive). Mr Morgan Petty, what unrivalled opportunities
this could afford you for protected Continental mobility.

Lord Trefgarne was most grateful for your acknowledgement of his aviation achievements, which is just the encouragement needed for his own project about which he has considered writing a book, TEACH YOURSELF STAR WARS AVIATION. I am sure that people as innovative as yourself and Roger, Mr Morgan Petty, will not wish to start from such a simple basis as sonic aviation, and Lord Trefgarne hopes your kind offer to make Roger available for pioneering flying exploits will extend to expeditions into the great unknown.

Exploration of Earth's great wildernesses have etched the names of Livingstone, Scott and Blashford-Snell into our history books and with his silk scarf and a pith helmet, which Lord Trefgarne would happily lend for protection from solar radiation and meteorites, I am sure that your friend Roger would feel confident enough to pilot the Squirrel (with necessary modifications) to the frontiers of our knowledge. What a challenge, Mr Morgan Petty; to bring peace and security where no man has gone before!

The rocket leaves on Friday; may Lord Trefgarne include your name and Roger's in the list of those who may be lucky enough to take their inventions on board it?

                    Yours sincerely

the house next door. Ingrid even asked her friend Katzie, who runs the feminist pottery, to make us some commemorative mugs. Unfortunately the feminist pottery hasn't been open very long, so they haven't had a great deal of practice, and the mugs, when they arrive, are not terribly good. However to show our appreciation we drink our mid-morning coffee out of them and put our jumpers in to soak afterwards. This merriment overshadows the bad news we have had from the Parachute Regiment who, it seems, are not in a position to sell us a secondhand parachute and suggest we try the R.A.F. instead. Still, earlier this week I did receive a reply from Geoffrey Pattie to the effect that the contents of my letter inviting him to buy our 'spare' Squirrel had been noted. I suppose they have to be careful with public money and are waiting to see how it performs in its air trials.

Tuesday, 21 February

I have received a letter from the Ministry of Defence, which offers me the use of an airship and protection by a Trident submarine. Having read it all I suspect the hand of a forger, although the notepaper and envelope look genuine enough. I tell Roger that it is in extremely poor taste, as defence is far too serious a subject to joke about.

Wednesday, 22 February

Away in the distance Mr Bridger's bonfire is glowing brightly against the winter sky and the Odette sisters are baking potatoes in foil at its base. Can it really only be a year since our momentous declaration? We have struggled against such odds and come through. Especially Roger, who only this morning, putting up the bunting, hit his thumb with the hammer and had to be rushed to hospital to have the nail off. However, I think I can safely say that we have set down a solid base from which to march onward. We still have the Challenger to look forward to, and the Squirrel, and of course the musical evening. It promises to be an exciting time, and if we are very, very lucky we might even attain the unthinkable: a reply from Mr Michael Heseltine.

Editor's note

Shortly after the first year of Morgan Petty's Defence Diary was completed, a letter arrived at 3 Cherry Drive from the Prime Minister's office. Sadly, it did not contain notification of Roger's knighthood. Its contents were, in fact, a double disappointment for Morgan Petty, but the letter is printed here to show there are no hard feelings – and perhaps Roger will have better luck next time.

At last a letter from No. 10!

10 DOWNING STREET

21 March 1984

Dear Mr Morgan Petty

Thank you for your recent letter to Bernard
Ingham which has been passed to me for reply. I
read it with interest and appreciate your inviting
the Prime Minister to your forthcoming celebration.
However, I am sure you will understand that with so
very many pressures upon her time, Mrs Thatcher is
not able to accept.

Thank you for writing.

Yours sincerely

ROMOLA CHRISTOPHERSON
Deputy Press Secretary

W Morgan Petty Esq